INTERNATIONAL SERIES OF MONOGRAPHS IN

INORGANIC CHEMISTRY

GENERAL EDITORS: H. TAUBE AND A. G. MADDOCK

VOLUME 3

AN INTRODUCTION TO CO-ORDINATION CHEMISTRY

OTHER TITLES IN THE SERIES IN INORGANIC CHEMISTRY

Vol. 1. CAGLIOTI (Ed.) – *Chemistry of the Co-ordination Compounds*

Vol. 2. VICKERY – *The Chemistry of Yttrium and Scandium*

Vol. 4. EBSWORTH – *Volatile Silicon Compounds*

AN INTRODUCTION TO

CO-ORDINATION CHEMISTRY

by

D. P. GRADDON

M.Sc., Ph.D., F.R.I.C.

Associate Professor of Inorganic Chemistry in the University of New South Wales

SECOND EDITION

PERGAMON PRESS

OXFORD · LONDON · EDINBURGH · NEW YORK
TORONTO · SYDNEY · PARIS · BRAUNSCHWEIG

Pergamon Press Ltd., Headington Hill Hall, Oxford
4 & 5 Fitzroy Square, London W.1
Pergamon Press (Scotland) Ltd., 2 & 3 Teviot Place, Edinburgh 1
Pergamon Press Inc., 44–01 21st Street, Long Island City, New York 11101
Pergamon of Canada, Ltd., 6 Adelaide Street East, Toronto, Ontario
Pergamon Press (Aust.) Pty. Ltd., Rushcutters Bay, Sydney, New South Wales
Pergamon Press S.A.R.L., 24 rue des Écoles, Paris 5e
Vieweg & Sohn GmbH, Burgplatz 1, Braunschweig

First edition 1961
Reprinted (with corrections) 1966
Second edition 1968

Library of Congress Catalog Card No. 67–31241

Filmset by The European Printing Corporation Ltd., Dublin,
and printed in Great Britain by D. R. Hillman and Sons Ltd.,
Frome, Somerset.
08 003237 0

CONTENTS

PREFACE TO SECOND EDITION

IN THE seven years since the first edition of this book appeared, co-ordination chemistry appears to have entered a phase of consolidation rather than revolution. This has been marked by the appearance of a wide range of review articles in journals, series publications and in book form, and by the production of invaluable collections of data in a second edition of *Stability Constants* and a supplement to *Interatomic Distances*, both published by the Chemical Society. This has made it possible to restrict references to books and review articles, which now appear as further reading at the end of each chapter.

The historical matter in the first chapter has been slightly increased and the second chapter extended to include an outline of transition metal spectra in terms of crystal field theory. The third chapter has been completely replaced and now presents a survey of the stereochemistry of first-row transition metals. Changes made to the remaining chapters to bring them up to date include numerous tables of stability constant data in Chapter IV, some new data in Chapters V and VI and the co-ordination chemistry of some biological systems in Chapter VII.

Sydney,
July 1966

D.P.G.

CHAPTER I

HISTORICAL INTRODUCTION

HISTORICALLY, co-ordination chemistry is of comparatively recent origin. The earliest recorded co-ordination compound is probably prussian blue, obtained by the artists' colour maker, Diesbach, in Berlin during the first decade of the eighteenth century. Its discovery, like so many important events in the history of chemistry, was accidental, the blue pigment being obtained as a by-product when animal refuse and soda were heated in an iron pot. Iron was also involved in the accidental discovery of three other types of co-ordination compound: the carbonyls in 1891, the phthalocyanins in 1926 and the *cyclo*pentadienyls in 1951.

In 1753, by treating prussian blue with alkali, Macquer obtained "yellow prussiate of potash" [potassium hexacyanoferrate(II)] from which, thirty years later, Scheele isolated prussic acid, describing among other properties its smell and taste and surviving, miraculously, to report his results. Another early example of the use of co-ordination compounds, dating from about 1760, was Lewis's method of refining platinum through the sparingly-soluble potassium hexachloroplatinate(IV).

However, the beginning of co-ordination chemistry is usually dated from the discovery of the cobalt(III) ammines by Tassaert in 1798. Tassaert observed that ammoniacal solutions of cobalt(II) chloride when allowed to stand overnight, deposited orange crystals of a compound with the formula $CoCl_3.6NH_3$. In this compound he recognized a new type of chemical substance formed by combination of two compounds, each of which was already fully saturated and capable of an independent existence. The properties of the new "complex" compound were quite different from those of either of its constituents.

During the following half century increasing numbers of these complex compounds were obtained, including many more cobalt(III) complexes and some derived from other elements, such as "red prussiate of potash" [potassium hexacyanoferrate(III)] in 1822, Magnus's green salt in 1828 and the nitroprussides in 1849.

The large number of cobalt(III) ammines known necessitated a system of naming and, as their structures were not understood, Fenny, in 1851–1852, introduced the familiar colour-code nomenclature, some examples of which are shown in Table 1.

TABLE 1. COLOUR-CODE NOMENCLATURE

Formula	Colour	Name
$CoCl_3.6NH_3$	yellow	*luteo*cobaltic chloride
$CoCl_3.5NH_3$	purple	*purpureo*cobaltic chloride
$CoCl_3.5NH_3.H_2O$	red	*roseo*cobaltic chloride
$CoCl_3.4NH_3$	green	*praseo*cobaltic chloride
$Co(NO_2)_3.5NH_3$	brown	*xantho*cobaltic nitrite

At this time several theories were proposed to explain the nature of these complex compounds. As nineteenth-century chemistry was all of one piece and not subdivided into the artificial sections which are usual today, the sort of theories developed to account for complex compounds were similar to those which were in current use in contemporary organic chemistry. Thus in 1837 Graham, who had been working on the basicity of acids, suggested that the cobalt ammines should be regarded as ammonium salts in which one of the hydrogen atoms of the NH_4 group was replaced by the metal atom. This idea comes remarkably close to the Lewis-acid–base approach to co-ordination compounds of nearly a century later.

During the period 1840–1860, the classification of organic compounds was developed largely on the basis of the "type" theory, which was enunciated in its final form by Gerhard in 1853. In 1854 Claus put forward views on the nature of complex salts which are clearly related to the sort of view of chemical compounds taken by the type theory: he drew the parallel between complex salts, such as the cobalt(III) ammines and salt hydrates, which he regarded as the same type of compound but with water in place of ammonia. Claus also recognized that the usual properties of both the ammonia and the metal were submerged in the complex ammines, though the equivalence of the metal was unaffected.

One of the major problems of organic chemists in the middle of the nineteenth century was to provide some structural explanation for the occurrence of homologous series. The parallel between homologous series and the metal ammines is made very obvious if we write both out as generalized formulae, for example:

$$CH_3.(CH_2)_n.Cl$$

$$Co.(NH_3)_n.Cl_3$$

and so the solution which Kekulé provided to the organic chemists' problem was quickly carried over to the apparently analogous series of inorganic compounds. In 1858 Kekulé proposed that the successive members of an homologous series were related to one another like different lengths of a chain, each —CH_2— unit being a link in the chain. Within a few years Blomstrand suggested that the complex ammines were similarly related, the complexes $PtCl_2.4NH_3$ and $CoCl_2.6NH_3$, for example, being written thus:

$$\mathrm{Pt}\begin{matrix}\diagup\mathrm{NH_3.NH_3.Cl}\\ \\ \diagdown\mathrm{NH_3.NH_3.Cl}\end{matrix} \qquad\qquad \mathrm{Co}\begin{matrix}\diagup\mathrm{NH_3.NH_3.NH_3.Cl}\\ \\ \diagdown\mathrm{NH_3.NH_3.NH_3.Cl}\end{matrix}$$

I II

Formulae of this sort could be arranged so as to account for the increasing evidence of abnormalities in the behaviour of some of these compounds. Thus, when it was found that only two-thirds of the chlorine in purpureocobaltic chloride was precipitated by silver nitrate, this was explained by Jorgensen by suggesting that the reactive chlorine atoms were situated at the ends of ammonia chains, but the inactive one was directly attached to the metal atom (III).

$$\mathrm{Co}\begin{matrix}\diagup\mathrm{Cl}\\ \mathrm{—NH_3.NH_3.NH_3.NH_3.Cl}\\ \diagdown\mathrm{NH_3.Cl}\end{matrix} \qquad \mathrm{SO_4.Cu}\begin{matrix}\diagup\mathrm{OH_2—OH_2}\diagdown\\ \qquad\qquad\quad \mathrm{OH_2}\\ \diagdown\mathrm{OH_2—OH_2}\diagup\end{matrix}$$

III IV

During the period 1870–1880 organic chemists were particularly interested in ring compounds, and were able to achieve syntheses of rings of various sizes by quite simple reactions such as the Wurtz synthesis. In 1879, evidently applying similar ideas to inorganic compounds, Wurtz suggested that salt hydrates might be ring structures related to the ammines in the same sort of way as cyclic paraffins are related to the open chain compounds; thus the formula (IV) was proposed for copper(II) sulphate pentahydrate.

While these ideas about chain and ring molecules laid the foundations on which organic chemistry advanced very rapidly, their extension to inorganic chemistry was most unfortunate, and undoubtedly delayed the development of our understanding of the structure of inorganic compounds for many years.

The impulse for the final unravelling of these structural problems came in the end from the much earlier ideas of Berzelius about the electrical nature of matter. These ideas were finally crystallized by Arrhenius in 1887 when he put forward the conception of ions and it was only four years after this that Werner published the first of his two papers which together form the foundation of modern co-ordination chemistry.

WERNER'S THEORY

In his first paper on complex compounds, published in 1891, Werner questioned the then accepted hypothesis that all atoms had available for use a small fixed number of valencies, and suggested that the valency or combining power of an atom might be spread all over the surface of the atom and subdivided into units of differing strength. This idea he developed two years later into the concept of "primary" and "secondary" valencies, and in one form or another this concept has remained the basis of the chemistry of complex compounds.

According to Werner's definition, the "primary" valencies were those involved in satisfying the chemical equivalence of the atom, and the "secondary" valencies were those by which additional "co-ordinated" molecules were attached.

Thus, in luteocobaltic chloride, $CoCl_3.6NH_3$, for example, the chemical equivalence of the cobalt is satisfied by the three chlorine atoms, which are thus attached by three primary valencies. The ammonia molecules, which are said to be co-ordinated are attached by six secondary valencies. In the same way the five ammonia molecules and the water molecule are attached by six secondary valencies in roseocobaltic chloride, $CoCl_3.5NH_3.H_2O$.

When this compound is heated it loses water to give the purpureocobaltic chloride, $CoCl_3.5NH_3$. This compound differs from the two previous compounds in that silver nitrate precipitates only two-thirds of the chlorine from solution. This, we have already seen, was explained by Jorgensen in terms of the chain theory by supposing that one of the chlorine atoms was attached directly to the metal atom. Werner's explanation is that one of the chlorine atoms has become attached by a secondary valency, replacing the lost water molecule.

When praseocobaltic chloride, $CoCl_3.4NH_3$, reacts with silver nitrate only one-third of the chlorine is precipitated, thus suggesting that two of the chlorine atoms are attached by secondary valencies. By such observations Werner was led to conclude that in the cobalt(III) ammines the cobalt atom always had six secondary valencies, and they were always *all* used, though the primary valencies apparently did not always have to be used so long as the atoms which satisfied the chemical equivalence of the metal were attached by secondary valencies instead. The number of secondary valencies, which determines the maximum number of molecules which can be co-ordinated, is called the co-ordination number.

One of the consequences of this explanation is that it should be possible to obtain a compound $CoCl_3.3NH_3$ in which the six secondary valencies alone are sufficient for attachment of all the chlorine atoms and ammonia molecules. There are, therefore, no primary valencies in use and silver nitrate should precipitate none of the chlorine from this compound. The chain theory could not provide a structure for this compound in which all the chlorine would be attached directly to the metal atom and still leave one of the three valencies free for attachment of the ammonia chain, and so the properties of this compound would be a testing point for the rival theories. The fact that the compound $CoCl_3.3NH_3$ could not be prepared was a serious blow for Werner's theory, and delayed its general acceptance for many years.

The application of Arrhenius's ideas to complex compounds leads to a deeper understanding of the difference between Werner's primary and secondary valencies. Werner investigated many complex compounds by the conductivity method. He found that in a series of compounds such as $CoCl_3.6NH_3$, $CoCl_3.5NH_3$, $CoCl_3.4NH_3$, the conductivity decreased as the number of primary valencies in use decreased. The conclusion he drew was that attachment by primary valencies still allowed ionization to occur, whereas attachment by secondary valencies makes ionization impossible. The solution behaviour of the above compounds thus suggests the formation of complex ions:

$$CoCl_3.6NH_3 \rightarrow [Co(NH_3)_6]^{3+} + 3Cl^-$$
$$CoCl_3.5NH_3 \rightarrow [Co(NH_3)_5Cl]^{2+} + 2Cl^-$$
$$CoCl_3.4NH_3 \rightarrow [Co(NH_3)_4Cl_2]^{+} + Cl^-$$

Although the crucial compound, $CoCl_3.3NH_3$ could not be made, Werner obtained several series of compounds which included species which were non-electrolytes. Three examples of such series are:

$Co(NO_2)_3.6NH_3$	$PtCl_4.6NH_3$	$PtCl_2.4NH_3$
$Co(NO_2)_3.5NH_3$	$PtCl_4.5NH_3$	$PtCl_2.3NH_3$
$Co(NO_2)_3.4NH_3$	$PtCl_4.4NH_3$	$PtCl_2.2NH_3$
$Co(NO_2)_3.3NH_3$	$PtCl_4.3NH_3$	$PtCl_2.NH_3.KCl$
$Co(NO_2)_3.2NH_3.KNO_2$	$PtCl_4.2NH_3$	$PtCl_2.2KCl$
$Co(NO_2)_3.NH_3.2KNO_2$	$PtCl_4.NH_3.KCl$	
$Co(NO_2)_3.3KNO_2$	$PtCl_4.2KCl$	

Figure 1 shows the conductivities of the complete series of platinum(IV) compounds including the non-electrolyte $[PtCl_4(NH_3)_2]$. Similar diagrams have been obtained for the compounds in the other two series in which the non-electrolytes are $[Co(NO_2)_3(NH_3)_3]$ and $[Pt(NH_3)_2Cl_2]$.

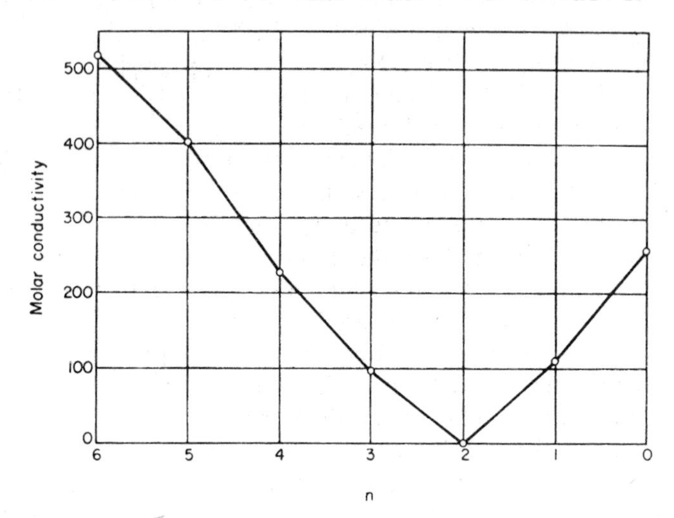

FIG. 1. Molar conductivities of the platinum-IV complexes $Pt(NH_3)_n Cl_4$ and $K_{2-n}Pt(NH_3)_nCl_{6-n}$, showing $[Pt(NH_3)_2Cl_4]$ as a non-electrolyte.

In this way it was shown that precipitation by silver nitrate of two-thirds and one-third of the chlorine in $CoCl_3.5NH_3$ and $CoCl_3.4NH_3$ corresponds with the formation of three and two ions in solution, thus confirming the suggested formulae:

$$[Co(NH_3)_5Cl]^{2+}\ 2Cl^-$$
$$[Co(NH_3)_4Cl_2]^+\ Cl^-$$

The formulae of the compounds which contain no ammonia must be written with the metal atoms in a complex anion, thus:

$$[Co(NO_2)_6]^{3-}\ 3K^+$$
$$[PtCl_6]^{2-}\ 2K^+$$

and in every case all six secondary valencies remain in use, though the number of primary valencies used varies from compound to compound, and becomes zero in the non-electrolyte compounds:

$$[Co(NH_3)_3(NO_2)_3]^0$$
$$[Pt(NH_3)_2Cl_4]^0$$
$$[Pt(NH_3)_2Cl_2]^0$$

By experiments of this sort it is possible to discover which atoms or groups are part of the complex ion or molecule and which are associated anions or cations. Present-day systematic nomenclature of complex compounds is based on this knowledge.

Bridged Complexes

Among the compounds known to or made by Werner were some in which the number of co-ordinated groups appeared to be insufficient to satisfy all the secondary valencies of the metal atom. This difficulty was overcome by proposing that some of the groups formed bridges between two metal atoms. A series of reactions by which bridged cobalt(III) compounds of this type can be obtained is shown below:

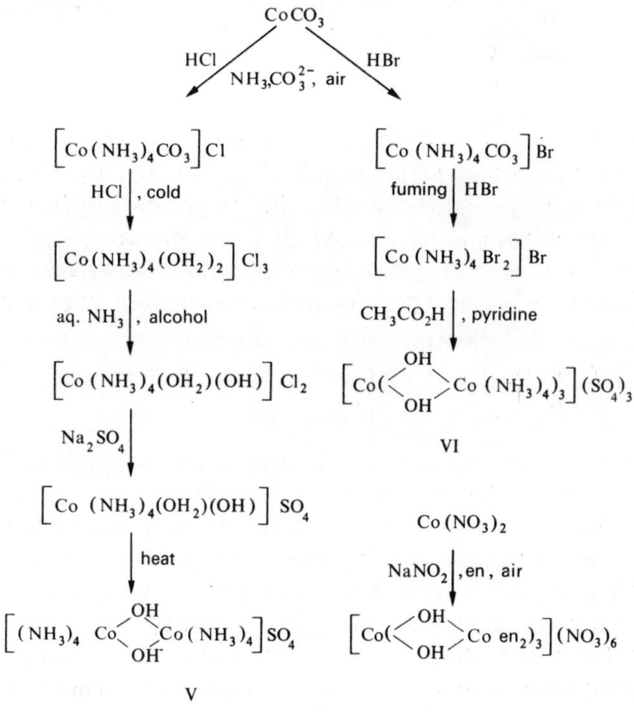

$CoCO_3$ (HCl; NH_3, CO_3^{2-}, air; HBr)

$[Co(NH_3)_4CO_3]Cl$ — HCl, cold → $[Co(NH_3)_4(OH_2)_2]Cl_3$ — aq. NH_3, alcohol → $[Co(NH_3)_4(OH_2)(OH)]Cl_2$ — Na_2SO_4 → $[Co(NH_3)_4(OH_2)(OH)]SO_4$ — heat → $[(NH_3)_4Co(OH)_2Co(NH_3)_4]SO_4$

V

$[Co(NH_3)_4CO_3]Br$ — fuming HBr → $[Co(NH_3)_4Br_2]Br$ — CH_3CO_2H, pyridine → $[Co((OH)_2Co(NH_3)_4)_3](SO_4)_3$

VI

$Co(NO_3)_2$ — $NaNO_2$, en, air → $[Co((OH)_2Co\,en_2)_3](NO_3)_6$

It will be observed that in the intermediate carbonate complex the carbonate group has to occupy two co-ordination sites if the co-ordination number of the cobalt atom is to be maintained at six. Although this involves forming a four-membered ring, it has since been confirmed by X-ray analysis that this complex ion does contain such a ring.

The final compounds in this series of reactions have empirical formulae which can be expressed as $Co(NH_3)_4(OH)SO_4$ and $Co_4(NH_3)_{12}(OH)_6(SO_4)_3$. In both cases the sulphate groups react immediately with barium salts and so must be considered to be outside the complex. The bridged structures V and VI allow all the metal atoms to remain 6:co-ordinate.

In these examples the cobalt atoms are bridged by two hydroxyl groups. Compounds are also known in which other groups act as bridges and the number of bridging groups may be either one, two or three. Thus the oxidation of ammoniacal cobalt(II) nitrate solution by air and subsequent neutralization by sulphuric acid gives a product known as Vortmann's salt, which has been found to be a mixture of which the main constituent is the bridged complex (VII).

$$[(NH_3)_4Co\genfrac{}{}{0pt}{}{\diagup NH_2 \diagdown}{\diagdown OH \diagup}Co(NH_3)_4](SO_4)_2$$

VII

$$[(NH_3)_5Co.O_2.Co(NH_3)_5](NO_3)_4$$

VIII

If the ammoniacal cobalt(II) nitrate solution is oxidized and then allowed to deposit crystals, another bridged complex (VIII) is obtained. This compound has only a single bridging group, which is a peroxide ion, O_2^{2-}, co-ordinated at each end. It forms brown crystals which explode on heating to 200°C, liberate oxygen when treated with cold sulphuric acid, and chlorine with hot concentrated hydrochloric acid.

SYSTEMATIC NOMENCLATURE

In the systematic nomenclature of inorganic compounds, cations are placed before anions, polyatomic anions are ended "-ate" and the oxidation states of those elements which have variable oxidation states are included as Roman figures in brackets immediately following the element. Thus ferric chloride becomes iron(III) chloride and potassium permanganate becomes potassium manganate(VII).

As Werner demonstrated, in complex compounds the metal atom may be present in either cation or anion, or in an uncharged molecule. Furthermore, it may have attached to it a variety of co-ordinated atoms or groups, now usually known as ligands. The systematic name for a complex compound must show the oxidation state of the metal atom, whether the metal atom is present in an anion or cation, the number of each type of ligand within the complex and whether the ligands are neutral molecules or anions. This is achieved by the following rules:

(1) If the ligands inside a complex are neutral molecules, they have their usual names except that ammonia is written "ammine" and water is written "aquo".

(2) If the ligands are anions, their names end in "-o", thus: chloro, bromo, nitro, sulphato. (Aquo is an exception, tolerated because of tradition.)

(3) When listing the ligands in a complex ion, anions are placed first, followed by neutral ligands. There are strict rules of precedence, the most common ligands being arranged in the order: hydroxo, chloro, nitro, organic anions, aquo, ammine, inorganic molecules, organic molecules.

(4) The names of ligands inside a complex are placed before the metal atom; the number of each sort of ligand is indicated by a prefix. The name of the metal atom is followed by its oxidation state and then by the names of any associated anions.

(5) If the complex is an anion, the name of the metal is ended "-ate", and the names of associated cations are placed before the name of the complex ion.

The examples in Table 2 will illustrate the principles of systematic nomenclature.

TABLE 2. SYSTEMATIC NOMENCLATURE

Formula	Systematic name
$[Co(NH_3)_6]^{3+}3Cl^-$	hexamminecobalt(III) chloride
$[Co(NH_3)_5(H_2O)]^{3+}3Cl^-$	aquopentamminecobalt(III) chloride
$[Co(NH_3)_5Cl]^{2+}2Cl^-$	chloropentamminecobalt(III) chloride
$[Co(NH_3)_4(NO_2)_2]^+NO_2^-$	dinitrotetramminecobalt(III) nitrite
$[Co(NH_3)_3(NO_2)_3]$	trinitrotriamminecobalt(III)
$[Pt(NH_3)_2Cl_2]$	dichlorodiammineplatinum(II)
$K[Pt(NH_3)Cl_5]$	potassium pentachloroammineplatinate(IV)
$K_2[PtCl_6]$	potassium hexachloroplatinate(IV)
$Na_3[Co(NO_2)_6]$	sodium hexanitrocobaltate(III)

ISOMERISM

One of the features of the chemistry of complex compounds is the formation of isomers. Isomerism, the existence of several different compounds with the same empirical formula, arises from the possibility of interchanging ligands within a complex ion with associated anions or molecules. Numerous possibilities exist for such interchanges, all similar in principle, but the historical development of co-ordination chemistry and the importance of isomerism in establishing the nature of complex compounds has led to the use of specific names for each slightly different variation. The more important types of isomerism which have been thus distinguished are as follows:

Ionization Isomerism

This type of isomerism involves interchange of a ligand anion with an associated anion outside the complex.

Aquopentamminecobalt(III) bromide, like the corresponding chloride mentioned above, loses water on heating to give bromopentamminecobalt(III) bromide which with silver sulphate gives a precipitate of silver bromide and a solution from which the corresponding bromopentamminecobalt(III) sulphate (IX) can be obtained.

Chloropentamminecobalt(III) chloride reacts with concentrated sulphuric acid to give a sulphatopentammine bisulphate from which, by reaction with barium bromide, sulphatopentamminecobalt(III) bromide (X) is obtained.

$$[Co(NH_3)_5(H_2O)]Br_3 \rightarrow [Co(NH_3)_5Br]Br_2 \rightarrow \underset{IX}{[Co(NH_3)_5Br]SO_4}$$

$$[Co(NH_3)_5Cl]Cl_2 \rightarrow [Co(NH_3)_5(SO_4)]SO_4H \rightarrow \underset{X}{[Co(NH_3)_5(SO_4)]Br}$$

Compounds (IX) and (X) are isomers, related by interchange of the bromide and sulphate ions. Compound (IX) with the bromide ion inside the complex, gives a precipitate of barium sulphate when treated with soluble barium salts, but does not react with silver nitrate. Compound (X) with the sulphate ion inside the complex, reacts with silver salts but not with barium salts.

Another example of this type of isomerism is provided by the compounds $[Pt(NH_3)_4Cl_2]Br_2$ and $[Pt(NH_3)_4Br_2]Cl_2$.

Solvate Isomerism

During the period 1900–1920 a considerable amount of work was done on hydrated chromium(III) salts. It was found that many of these compounds could be obtained in isomeric forms by different methods of preparation. Usually one of the isomers was purple-violet in colour and the others green. Groups of isomers studied include the chloride, bromide, sulphate and phosphate; the chloride may be taken as characteristic.

Crystallization of chromium(III) chloride from acidified aqueous solutions gives a dark-green form of the hydrate, $CrCl_3.6H_2O$; a light green form with the same formula is obtained by precipitating a solution of chromium(III) chloride sulphate, $CrClSO_4$, with ether; when hydrogen chloride gas is passed into a freshly prepared solution of chromium(III) alum a violet form of the chloride hexahydrate is obtained.

Treatment of freshly prepared solutions of the three isomers with silver nitrate solution produces different results: all the chlorine is precipitated from the violet isomer, two-thirds from the light green isomer and only one-third from the dark green isomer. Exposure of the violet isomer over sulphuric acid in a desiccator produces no change, but under these conditions the light green isomer loses one molecule of water and the dark green isomer loses two. Clearly, the three isomers can be represented by the following formulae:

violet form	$[Cr(H_2O)_6]^{3+}3Cl^-$
light green form	$[Cr(H_2O)_5Cl]^{2+}2Cl^-.H_2O$
dark green form	$[Cr(H_2O)_4Cl_2]^+Cl^-.2H_2O$

It is important that the reactions with silver nitrate be carried out on freshly prepared solutions as the complex ions undergo slow replacement reactions in solution, for example:

$$[Cr(H_2O)_5Cl^-]^{2+} + H_2O \rightleftharpoons [Cr(H_2O)_6]^{3+} + Cl^-$$

Studies of the colours of solutions of these compounds show that eventually an equilibrium mixture of isomers is produced. The composition of the equilibrium solution depends upon the concentration: as might be expected, at very low concentrations the chromium is present at equilibrium almost wholly as the hexaquo ion, $[Cr(H_2O)_6]^{3+}$, but at higher concentrations the proportion of chloro-complexes increases.

When, as in this case, solvate isomerism involves replacement of a ligand anion or molecule by water molecules, it is often referred to as hydrate isomerism.

Co-ordination Isomerism

An extreme case of ionization isomerism arises when both anion and cation are complex. It is then possible to interchange some or all of the ligands in one complex ion for those in the other. An example of this is the two compounds represented by the formulae:

$$[Co(NH_3)_6]^{3+}\,[Cr(CN)_6]^{3-}$$
$$[Cr(NH_3)_6]^{3+}\,[Co(CN)_6]^{3-}$$

Similar in appearance, each of these compounds gives a precipitate of complex cyanide when treated with silver nitrate solution, but from the first compound the precipitate contains chromium and the solution cobalt, whereas from the second compound silver precipitates the cobalt and chromium remains in solution.

Another example of this type of isomerism is provided by combination of the various ions in the cobalt(III) nitro-ammine series mentioned above. The following quite distinct compounds are co-ordinate isomers:

$$[Co(NH_3)_6]^{3+} [Co(NO_2)_6]^{3-}$$
$$[Co(NH_3)_4(NO_2)_2]^{+} [Co(NH_3)_2(NO_2)_4]^{-}$$

An example taken from the 4:co-ordinate platinum(II) chloro-ammine series includes the co-ordinate isomers with the following formulae:

$$[Pt(NH_3)_4]^{2+} [PtCl_4]^{2-}$$
$$[Pt(NH_3)_3Cl]^{+} [Pt(NH_3)Cl_3]^{-}$$

and a larger group of isomers of this type can be obtained if one of the ions contains platinum and one palladium:

$$[Pt(NH_3)_4]^{2+} [PdCl_4]^{2-}$$
$$[Pt(NH_3)_3Cl]^{+} [Pd(NH_3)Cl_3]^{-}$$
$$[Pd(NH_3)_3Cl]^{+} [Pt(NH_3)Cl_3]^{-}$$
$$[Pd(NH_3)_4]^{2+} [PtCl_4]^{2-}$$

Polymerization Isomerism

Continuation of the series of cobalt(III) or platinum(II) compounds above gives as the next member of the series a neutral molecule containing equal numbers of ammonia molecules and nitro or chloro anions as ligands. These neutral compounds:

$$[Co(NH_3)_3(NO_2)_3]^{0}$$
$$[Pt(NH_3)_2Cl_2]^{0}$$

are also isomers of the salts in the respective series, and indeed the last compound can be obtained simply by the action of heat on the doubly complex salts.

The neutral compounds, however, although they have the same empirical formulae as the doubly complex salts, have smaller formula weights. The doubly complex salts have formula weights which are double those of the neutral molecules.

This type of isomerism, in which one compound has the same empirical formula as another, but a formula weight which is a multiple of that of the other, is known as polymerization isomerism. Another example can be obtained from the series of platinum(IV) chloro-ammine complexes mentioned above. In the following list the multiple of the empirical formula is also indicated:

$[Pt(NH_3)_2Cl_4]$	XI
$[Pt(NH_3)_4Cl_2]^{2+} [PtCl_6]^{2-}$	X2
$2[Pt(NH_3)_5Cl]^{3+} 3[PtCl_6]^{2-}$	X5
$[Pt(NH_3)_6]^{4+} 2[PtCl_6]^{2-}$	X3

Rather similar to this type of isomerism is a sort of polymerization, not recognized during the early development of co-ordination chemistry, in which a neutral molecule can exist either as a simple monomer or as a polymer in which the metal atom has a higher co-ordination number. An example, discussed on p. 78, is provided by the two forms of dichlorodipyridinecobalt(II).

Structural Isomerism

An unusual type of isomerism is observed in the compound nitropentamminecobalt(III) chloride. A red form of this compound is obtained when chloropentamminecobalt(III) chloride is treated with dilute nitrous acid. This red form is not stable to acids, which convert it to a brown form. The brown form is also obtained when nitrous fumes react with ammoniacal solutions of cobalt(II) chloride.

The chlorides of the red and brown forms both give complete precipitation of all their chlorine with silver nitrate, so there is no case of ionization isomerism and both cations must be given the formula, $[Co(NH_3)_5NO_2]^{2+}$.

It is now known that the difference between these isomers is that in the red form the NO_2^- ion within the complex is attached to the cobalt atom through an oxygen atom, whereas in the brown form the NO_2^- ion is attached to the cobalt through the nitrogen atom. These isomers are thus related in the same way as organic nitrites and nitro-compounds and are named accordingly:

$[(NH_3)_5Co{-}ONO]^{2+}$ nitritopentamminecobalt(III) ion

$$\left[(NH_3)_5Co{-}N\begin{smallmatrix}\nearrow O\\ \searrow O\end{smallmatrix}\right]^{2+}$$ nitropentamminecobalt(III) ion

There are several other ligands with which we might expect to observe this type of structural isomerism, notably the cyanide and thiocyanate ions. However, although compounds are known in which thiocyanate ions are attached to metal atoms by the nitrogen atom and others in which attachment is through the sulphur atom, there does not appear to be any case in which both possible isomeric forms of a particular compound have been isolated; in the case of cyanide complexes it is doubtful whether any case of co-ordination through the nitrogen atom is known. Many compounds are now known in which cyanide or thiocyanate ions are co-ordinated at both ends, thus forming bridges between two metal atoms.

STEREOCHEMISTRY OF 6:CO-ORDINATE COMPOUNDS

The presence in a complex compound of six groups attached by secondary valencies to the metal atom raises a similar stereochemical problem to that posed to the organic chemists by the molecule of benzene. As in this earlier example there are three reasonable structures to choose from: the flat hexagon (XI), the trigonal prism (XII), and the octahedron (XIII), each with the metal atom in the middle. As in the case of benzene, the choice was made on the basis of the number of stereoisomers obtainable with molecules or ions of the form MA_nB_{6-n}.

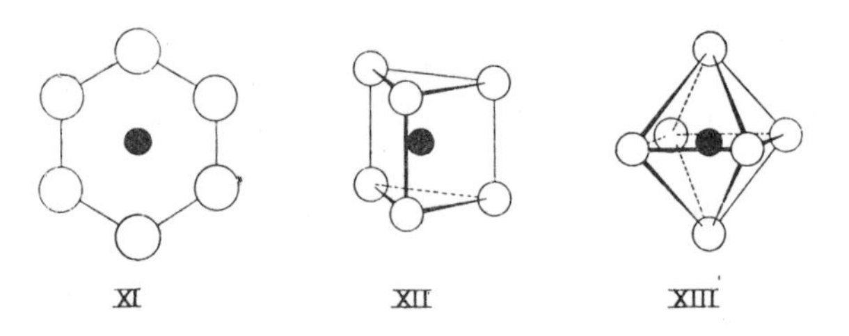

XI XII XIII

Cis–trans Isomerism

The most important compounds affecting the distinction between the stereochemical possibilities were those of the type MA_4B_2, which should exist in three isomeric forms if hexagonal or trigonal prismatic, but only two if octahedral, the *cis* (XIV) and *trans* (XV):

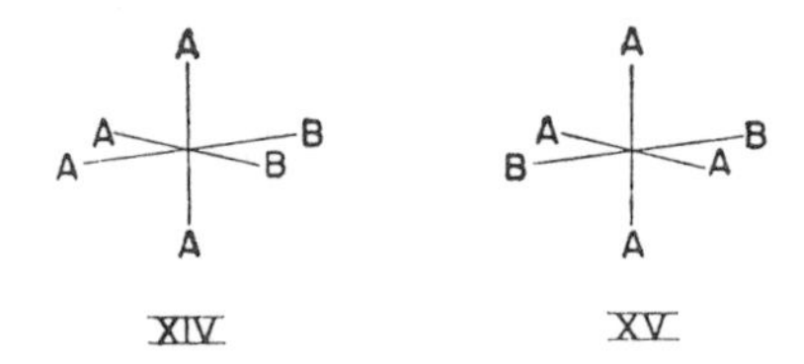

XIV XV

Numerous compounds of this type are now known in two isomeric forms, but none in more than two, indicating the octahedral structure, later confirmed by much other evidence, including numerous X-ray analyses.

In most cases the *cis*-isomers are less stable than the *trans*-isomers, but they can sometimes be obtained by the displacement of a bidentate group (i.e. a group such as ethylenediamine which can co-ordinate twice to the same metal atom and must occupy two adjacent co-ordination positions).

One of the testing points of Werner's theory concerned the existence of a second isomer of praseocobaltic chloride, $[Co(NH_3)_4Cl_2]Cl$; at the time only the green (*trans*) isomer was known and all attempts to obtain another had failed. The second isomer, predicted by the theory, was eventually made by Werner by a series of reactions, the last of which involved replacement of a bidentate group by the two chlorine atoms (shown on p. 16).

Another example of *cis–trans* isomerism, in this case involving bidentate groups in the isomeric complex compounds, is provided by the two isomers of dithiocyanatobis(ethylenediamine)chromium(III) thiocyanate, $[Cr\ en_2(NCS)_2]^+\ NCS^-$. By the action of ethylenediamine on potassium hexathiocyanatochromate(III), $K_3Cr(NCS)_6$, this compound can be obtained in two forms, one green and one violet. Similarly coloured isomers are also known of the corresponding chlorides $[Cr\ en_2Cl_2]Cl$ and of the cobalt(III) compound $[Co\ en_2Cl_2]Cl$.

The two isomers can be distinguished by reaction with oxalates. The violet isomers react by replacement of chloride by oxalate, thus showing that the two chlorine atoms occupy *cis*-positions. The green *trans*-isomers do not react.

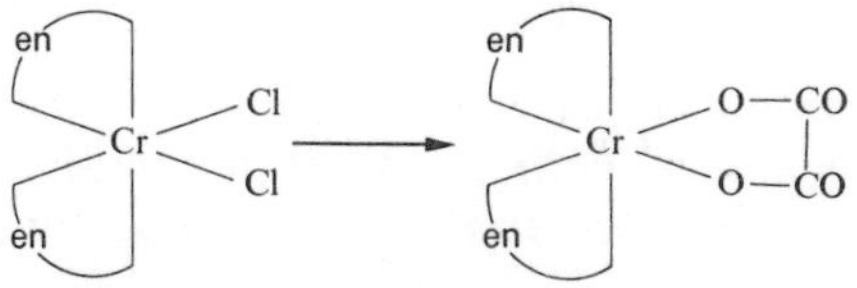

Optical Isomerism

The presence of three bifunctional groups in a complex leads to the possibility of optical isomerism. Such isomers, represented by the diagrams (XVI) and (XVII), were predicted by Werner and numerous examples were subsequently resolved by him, including the ions $[Co(en)_3]^{3+}$, $[Cr(en)_3]^{3+}$, $[Rh(en)_3]^{3+}$, $[Ir(en)_3]^{3+}$, $[Rh(C_2O_4)_3]^{3-}$ and $[Fe(dipy)_3]^{3+}$ (the abbreviations "en" and "dipy" represent ethylenediamine and 2:2′-dipyridyl, respectively).

When two bidentate groups and two single ligands are attached to the metal atom, combinations of optical and *cis–trans*-isomerism are possible, leading to three isomers: a *trans*-form (XVIII) with planes of symmetry and two optical isomers of the *cis*-form (XIX, XX).

The combination of these fundamental forms of stereoisomerism with one another and with the introduction of asymmetric organic molecules as ligands (e.g. propylenediamine), together with the possibilities of internal compensation (*meso*-forms) in polynuclear complexes leads to innumerable permutations which have been explored in much detail.

$CoCl_2$

↓ air, $(NH_4)_2CO_3$

$[Co(NH_3)_4(CO_3)]Cl$ $\xrightarrow{HCl}$ $[Co(NH_3)_4Cl_2]Cl$
trans-isomer
(green)

↓ dil. H_2SO_4

$[Co(NH_3)_4(OH_2)_2]^{3+}$

↓ dil. NH_4OH

$[Co(NH_3)_4(OH_2)(\bar{O}H)]^{2+}$

↘ $-H_2O$ (100°C)

$[(NH_3)_4Co(\bar{O}H)_2Co(NH_3)_4]^{4+}$

↓ −12°C conc. HCl

$[Co(NH_3)_4Cl_2]Cl$
cis-isomer
(violet)

While no purpose would be served by reproducing here a detailed account of these experiments, it is, perhaps, worth noting that in Werner's time optical activity was considered to be a phenomenon of organic chemistry

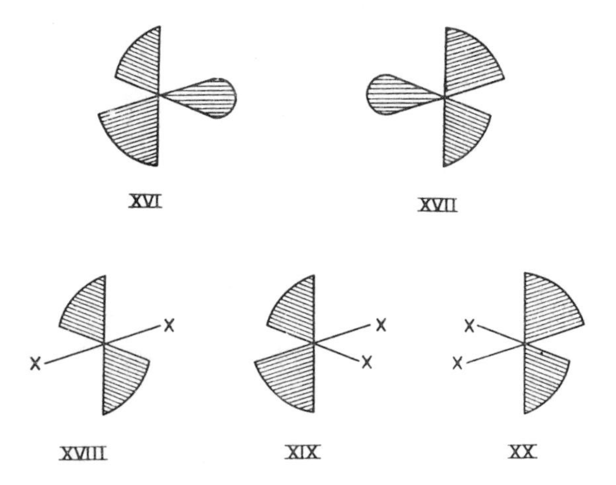

and there were still many who considered the optical activity of these complex compounds to be in some way due to the organic part of the molecule. Werner therefore prepared and resolved into optical isomers a wholly inorganic compound, containing the tetranuclear complex ion $[Co\{\begin{smallmatrix} OH \\ OH \end{smallmatrix} Co(NH_3)_4\}_3]^{6+}$, obtained by the action of ammonia on the salts of the ion $[Co(NH_3)_4(OH_2)Cl]^{2+}$.

STEREOCHEMISTRY OF 4:CO-ORDINATE COMPOUNDS

The formation of a yellow non-electrolyte, $[Pt(NH_3)_2Cl_2]$, from Magnus's green salt has been mentioned in connection with polymerization isomerism. This compound reacts with ammonia to form the tetrammine salt, $[Pt(NH_3)_4]Cl_2$, which when boiled with hydrochloric acid gives a non-electrolyte, $[Pt(NH_3)_2Cl_2]$, isomeric with the above compound, but differing from it in physical properties. These two isomers known, respectively, as the α- and β-diammine platinous chlorides, led Werner to the conclusion that the platinum atom, unlike the atoms commonly present in organic compounds, had square-planar stereochemistry.

On chemical grounds the β-isomer is assigned the *trans*-structure (XXI) and the α-isomer the *cis*-structure (XXII). The chemical evidence is considerable and complicated and only two examples of the numerous experiments on which the conclusions are based will be quoted, both based on the necessary *cis*-configuration of bidentate ligands:

(1) Both isomers react with moist silver oxide to give bases of the form $[Pt(NH_3)_2(OH)_2]$; oxalic acid displaces the hydroxyl groups and the α-isomer gives a non-electrolyte (XXIII), whereas the β-isomer gives a dibasic acid (XXIV) as the oxalate ion is unable to act as a bidentate group.

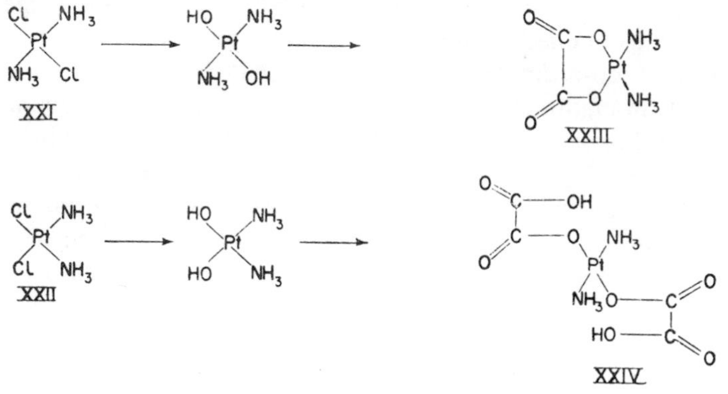

XXI → XXIII

XXII → XXIV

(2) The α-isomer reacts with ethylenediamine to form a tetrammine (XXV). An identical tetrammine is formed by the action of ammonia

on the non-electrolyte obtained from ethylenediamine and potassium chloroplatinite.

The square-planar structure and the allocation of configurations to the two isomers has been confirmed subsequently by X-ray analysis and by measurement of dipole moments. This last is a widely used method of physical determination of absolute configuration; perfectly symmetrical complexes of the *trans*-type, such as $[(R_3P)_2PtX_2]$, have zero dipole moments since the moments of individual bonds cancel one another; *cis*-isomers on the other hand have a resultant moment. One limitation of this method arises where the ligands do not have an axis of symmetry along the metal–ligand linkage (for example, primary amines); although the moments of the metal–ligand bonds will cancel in the *trans*-isomers of such compounds, there may be resultant moments across the plane of the molecule due to the asymmetry of the ligands themselves, but such moments are usually comparatively small.

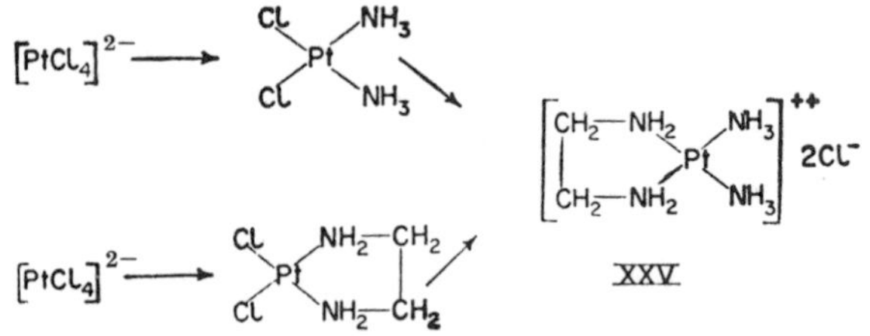

XXV

As with the 6:co-ordinated complexes the classical confirmation of the square-planar structure of platinous complexes was by isomer counts, in particular by the isolation of all three isomers of compounds of the type [PtABCD]; the alternative tetrahedral structure would give only two (optical) isomers. The first complete set of three isomers to be obtained was of the compound $[Pt(NH_3)(NO_2)(NH_2OH)(pyridine)]$ the three isomers being obtained by the reactions shown on p. 19.

As in the 6:co-ordinate compounds of cobalt(III), so in 4:co-ordinate compounds of platinum(II) there are numerous examples of maintenance of the co-ordination number by bridging. A simple example is the compound $Pt(NH_3)Cl_2$, obtained by evaporation of aqueous ammonium tetrachloroplatinate(II); though this particular compound has not been proved to have a bridged structure (XXVI), corresponding arsine and phosphine compounds have been shown to be dimeric in solution.

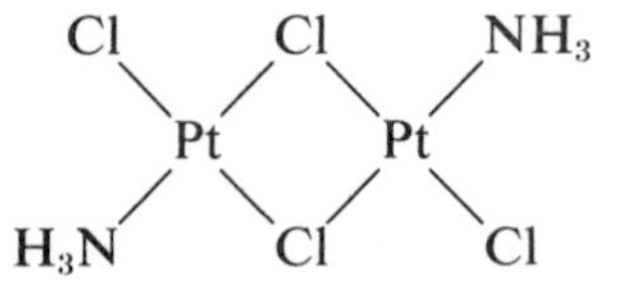

XXVI

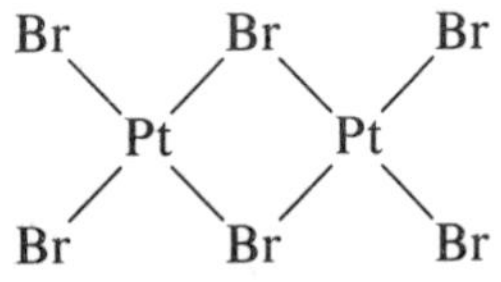

XXVII

$[Pt(NO_2)_4]^{=}$ → (NH_2OH) → $[Pt(O_2N)(NO_2)(HONH_2)(NO_2)]^-$ → (NH_2OH) → $[Pt(HONH_2)(NO_2)(HONH_2)(NO_2)]^0$

→ (NH_3) → $[Pt(HONH_2)(NH_3)(HONH_2)(NO_2)]^+$ → (HCl) → $[Pt(Cl)(NH_3)(HONH_2)(NO_2)]^0$ → (pyridine) → $[Pt(py)(NH_3)(HONH_2)(NO_2)]^+$

→ (pyridine) → $[Pt(HONH_2)(py)(HONH_2)(NO_2)]^+$ → (HCl) → $[Pt(Cl)(py)(HONH_2)(NO_2)]^0$ → (NH_3) → $[Pt(H_3N)(py)(HONH_2)(NO_2)]^+$

$[PtCl_4]^{=}$ → (pyridine) → $[Pt(Cl)(Cl)(Cl)(py)]^-$ → (NH_3) → $[Pt(H_3N)(Cl)(Cl)(py)]^0$ → (NO_2^-) → $[Pt(H_3N)(NO_2)(O_2N)(py)]^0$ → (HCl) → $[Pt(H_3N)(Cl)(O_2N)(py)]^0$ → (NH_2OH) → $[Pt(H_3N)(NH_2OH)(O_2N)(py)]^+$

The bridged halide anion $Pt_2Br_6^{2-}$ (XXVII) has been shown by X-ray analysis to occur in the tetraethylammonium salt of empirical formula $N(C_2H_5)_4PtBr_3$. In $PdCl_2$ and $PtCl_2$ polymers are formed (p. 67).

The stereochemistry of nickel(II) is more complicated, and will be discussed in detail in Chapter III. Amongst the complexes of nickel (II) are some in which the metal atom is 4:co-ordinate, but the range of such compounds is much smaller than with palladium and platinum, and their stereochemistry was not established until much later. Among these compounds one of the most familiar is the neutral complex bis(dimethylglyoximato)nickel(II), familiar for its use in gravimetric analysis. (XXVIII $R = R' = CH_3$.)

The square-planar stereochemistry of the nickel atom in compounds of this type was established by the isolation of cis and trans forms of the complexes with unsymmetrical glyoximes. Thus the benzylmethylglyoximate (XXVIII $R = CH_3$, $R' = CH_2C_6H_5$) was shown to occur in two isomeric forms with melting points 76°C and 168°C

XXVIII

and a number of other unsymmetrical glyoximates have also been obtained in two isomeric forms.

If the stereochemistry of the nickel atom were tetrahedral only one form would exist, and this form would have a dipole moment, as would the *cis*-form of a square-planar complex; the *trans*-square-planar complex, however, should have no dipole moment and this requirement has also been confirmed experimentally. The square-planar structure of bis(dimethylglyoximato)nickel(II) has been confirmed by X-ray analysis, which has also demonstrated the square configuration of a number of other 4:co-ordinate nickel(II) complexes, including the complex cyanide ion, $Ni(CN)_4^{2-}$.

The only other metal which consistently forms square planar complexes is gold in the oxidation state (III). Furthermore, gold(III) resembles palladium(II) and platinum(II) in that the square-planar co-ordination is preserved in all its compounds by the formation of bridged dimeric and polymeric units.

The auric halides, AuX_3, have been shown to be dimeric in non-donor solvents, though monomeric in donor solvents such as pyridine, which evidently co-ordinate in the fourth position. X-ray analysis of the chloride has shown that the dimers have a bridged structure with all the atoms in one plane and Au—Cl bonds longer in the bridge (2·33 Å) than in the terminal bonds (2·24 Å) (XXIX):

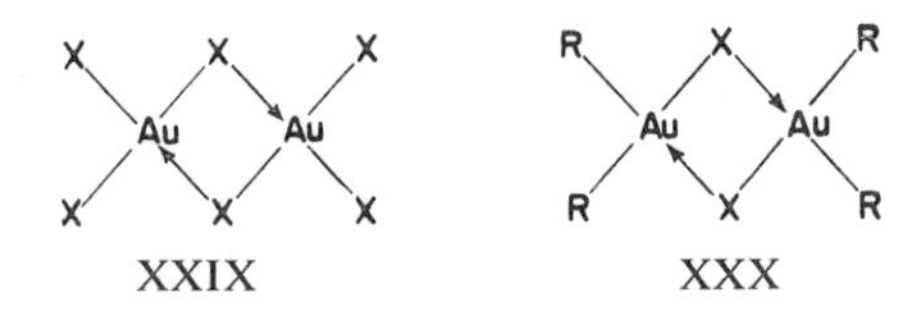

XXIX XXX

Treatment of the pyridine solutions of auric halides with Grignard reagents gives alkyl derivatives, but the trialkyls cannot be isolated from solution (owing to the difficulty of maintaining the co-ordination number);

the dialkyl halides are shown to be dimeric in non-donor solvents (XXX) and on treatment with silver sulphate give corresponding sulphates $(R_2Au)_2SO_4$, which are, rather surprisingly, also dimeric. With silver cyanide, the dialkyl gold cyanides, R_2AuCN, are formed; these are found to be tetrameric in solution and the structure (XXXI), based on the combination of the square planar co-ordination of the gold atoms with the linear bond distribution of the cyanide groups, has been confirmed by X-ray analysis. All of the atoms lie in the same plane.

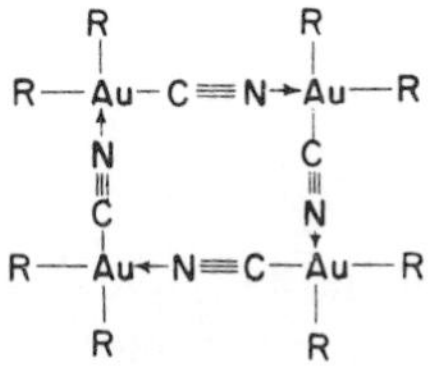

```
       R           R
       |           |
  R—Au—C≡N→Au—R
       ↑           |
       N           C
       ⦀           ⦀
       C           N
       |           ↓
  R—Au←N≡C—Au—R
       |           |
       R           R
```

XXXI

Though the structure of this tetrameric compound was originally predicted on the basis of square planar co-ordination of the gold atom, the square-planar stereochemistry of gold(III) was never proved by classical methods and appears to have been assumed by analogy with palladium(II) and platinum(II); it was first confirmed in 1934 by X-ray analysis of $KAuBr_4.2H_2O$, in which the $AuBr_4^-$ ion was shown to be square planar.

In the period from 1910 to 1940 there was much discussion of the stereochemistry of copper(II). Several claims were made to have achieved resolution of optical isomers of both 6: and 4:co-ordinate copper(II) complexes thus showing them to be octahedral or tetrahedral, and early X-ray studies were interpreted as showing square-planar co-ordination in such compounds as $CuCl_2.2H_2O$. The accumulation of crystal structure data on copper(II) complexes, however, has shown all these early claims to be incorrect and has revealed a unique and very complicated stereochemistry for this element. This will be described in detail in Chapter III.

The stereochemistry of one other metal was established by chemical methods. This is beryllium. Beryllium is almost invariably 4:co-ordinate in its complex compounds, and forms particularly stable complexes with ligands in which oxygen is the donor atom. In 1926 Mills and Gotts resolved optical isomers of the beryllium complex of the unsymmetrical bidentate oxygen donor benzoylpyruvic acid, thus showing that the beryllium complex (XXXII) was tetrahedral. Another beryllium complex with an unsymmetrical β-diketone, bis(benzoylacetonato)beryllium(II) (XXXIII) was resolved by Bailar and Busch in 1954, but this was after some other beryllium compounds had been shown to be tetrahedral by X-ray analysis.

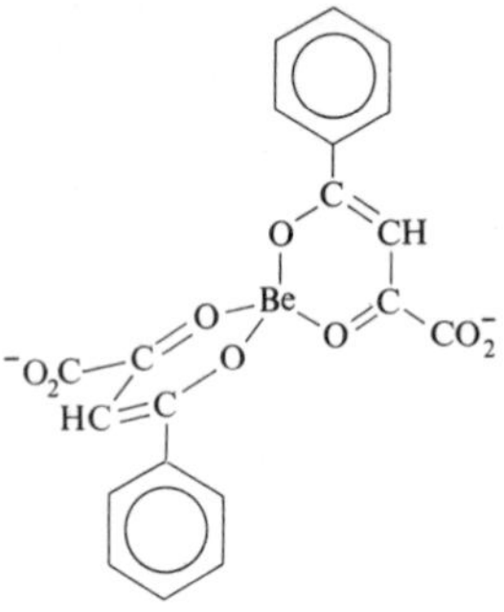

XXXII 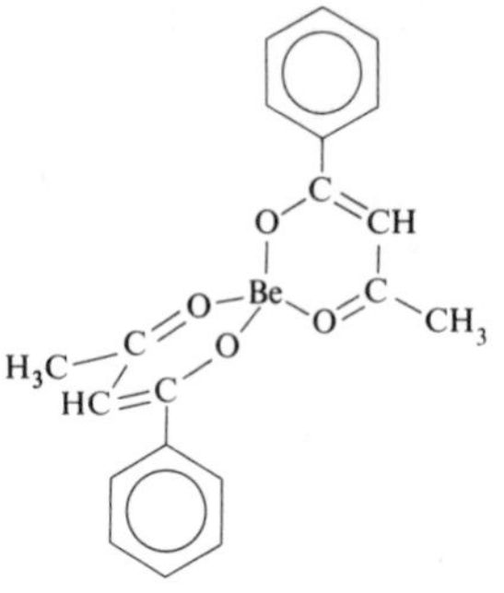 XXXIII

Crystal structure determinations have revealed several other metals which commonly form tetrahedral complex compounds. These include boron, aluminium, zinc and mercury; among transition metals only cobalt(II) forms large numbers of tetrahedral compounds. The compounds of most transition metals have been found to be predominantly 6:co-ordinate.

STEREOCHEMISTRY IN SOLUTION AND IN THE SOLID STATE

The achievements of isomerization studies based on Werner's theory were spectacular in establishing the stereochemistry of a small number of transition metals, in particular the octahedral stereochemistry of complexes of chromium(III), cobalt(III) and platinum(IV) and the square-planar structure of complexes of palladium(II) and platinum(II).

Apart from a few isolated octahedral complexes, such as those of iron, rhodium and iridium mentioned above, and a few planar complexes of nickel and the single tetrahedral complex of beryllium, however, these chemical methods were unable to extend our knowledge of stereochemistry to any other metallic elements. A broad knowledge of the stereochemistry of the remaining elements has had to await the accumulation of data obtained by X-ray analysis.

The reason for the failure to extend chemical methods to the other elements lies in the relative instability of the complexes of these elements. In order to isolate the *cis*- and *trans*-isomers of a complex or to resolve a mixture of *optical* isomers, these isomers must be stable enough to persist unchanged during the chemical reactions necessary for their isolation. Only a relatively small number of compounds is so stable.

However, the resolution of optical isomers or the isolation of geometrical isomers implies that the stereochemistry does survive chemical reactions and so must be preserved in solution. Classical methods of determining stereochemistry thus provide evidence, not only of the stereochemistry of the compounds isolated, but also of the stereochemistry of molecules and ions in solution.

Crystal structure studies by X-ray methods, on the other hand, although they can reveal the structure of complexes too unstable to be studied by chemical methods, tell us nothing about the stereochemistry of these compounds in solution. Indeed, many compounds are now known, the stereochemistry of which must be quite different in solution and in the solid state, as the properties of their solutions are not consistent with the crystal structures of the solid compounds. Some of these will be discussed in Chapter III.

FURTHER READING

EMELEUS, H. J. and ANDERSON, J. S., *Modern Aspects of Inorganic Chemistry*, 3rd ed., Routledge & Kegan Paul, London (1960).

MARTELL, A. E. and CALVIN, M., *Chemistry of the Metal Chelate Compounds*, Prentice-Hall, New York (1952).

MARTIN, D. F. and MARTIN, B. B., *Coordination Compounds*, McGraw-Hill, New York (1964).

DUNITZ, J. D. and ORGEL, L. E., Stereochemistry of ionic solids, *Advances Inorg. Chem., Radiochem.* **2**, 1 (1960).

KRISHNAMURTY, K. V. and HARRIS, G. M., The chemistry of the metal oxalato complexes, *Chem. Rev.* **61**, 213 (1961).

MELLOR, D. P., Historical background and fundamental concepts, *Chelating Agents and Metal Chelates*, Eds. MELLOR, D. P. and DWYER, F. P., Academic Press, New York (1964).

WILKINS, R. G. and WILLIAMS, M. J. G., The isomerism of complex compounds, *Modern Coordination Chemistry*, Eds. LEWIS, J. and WILKINS, R. G., Interscience, New York (1960).

CHAPTER II

MODERN THEORIES OF CO-ORDINATION CHEMISTRY

THE OCTET THEORY – EFFECTIVE ATOMIC NUMBER

Werner's theory was a landmark in the development of "complex" chemistry. It made it possible to understand the existence of hundreds of complex compounds, explained their stereochemistry, and made many predictions, particularly about their isomerism, which were subsequently confirmed experimentally. It remains the foundation on which any account of co-ordination compounds must be based. It could not, however, explain why certain elements had this remarkable ability to form numerous complex compounds, since the theory antedated by two decades the elucidation of the electronic structure of the atom, upon which all modern theoretical chemistry is founded.

We can now appreciate that the difference between Werner's primary and secondary valencies is the difference between ionic and covalent bonds. Thus, if we consider the typical series of ammines $[Co(NH_3)_4Cl_2]Cl$, $[Co(NH_3)_5Cl]Cl_2$ and $[Co(NH_3)_6]Cl_3$, the precipitation by silver nitrate of one, two and three atoms of chlorine, respectively, appears as evidence of the ionic binding of the corresponding number of chlorine atoms. The other chlorine atoms can be precipitated by silver nitrate after the prolonged action of alkali, a similar reaction to that required to cleave the carbon–halogen bonds in the alkyl halides.

The Co-ordinate Bond

To earlier generations one of the puzzling features of "complex" chemistry was the formation of chemical bonds between ions and complete molecules such as ammonia. This is readily explained by the electronic theory of atomic structure. In an ammonia molecule the nitrogen atom has a complete octet of electrons, six shared with the three hydrogen atoms to form covalent bonds, two unshared. In some other molecules, for instance boron fluoride, one of the atoms has two electrons less than are required to complete the octet. When molecules of ammonia react with molecules of boron fluoride the octet on the boron atom is completed by co-ordination of the unshared pair of electrons on the ammonia molecule:

$$\begin{array}{c}F\\|\\F-B\\|\\F\end{array} + \begin{array}{c}H\\|\\-N-H\\|\\H\end{array} = \begin{array}{c}F\ \ H\\|\ \ \ |\\F-B\leftarrow N-H\\|\ \ \ |\\F\ \ H\end{array}$$

The B—N bond so produced is a covalent bond, differing from an ordinary covalent bond in that both bonding electrons came originally from the same atom. This atom is referred to as the "donor" atom and the boron atom is the "acceptor" atom. Any molecule or ion having unshared pairs of electrons can act as a donor molecule and any ion or atom having an electronic structure which can be made up to an inert gas structure, or other stable electronic configuration, can act as an acceptor. The best-known examples of each type are:

Donors: neutral molecules of elements in groups VB, VIB and VIIB, e.g. NH_3, NR_3, OH_2, OR_2, SR_2, PR_3; anions of elements in groups VB, VIB, VIIB, e.g. NH_2^-, OH^-, F^-, Cl^-, Br^-, I^-; various other simple molecules or ions such as CO, CN^-.

Acceptors: neutral molecules of elements in group III, e.g. BF_3, $AlCl_3$, $B(CH_3)_3$; ions of the transition metals, e.g. Cr^{3+}, Fe^{2+}, Pt^{4+}, Cu^{2+}; H^+.

Co-ordination Number

Molecules such as boron fluoride or aluminium chloride can accept only one pair of electrons, but ions of the transition metals require larger numbers of electrons to bring their electronic structures up to that of the next inert gas and so can accommodate several donor groups (ligands). The number of ligands accommodated is known as the co-ordination number. The electronic structure of the metal atom in the complex then corresponds to that of another element; it is said to have the "effective atomic number" of this other element.

In the B subgroups of the periodic table the ions of elements in their group valency state all require eight electrons to reach the effective atomic number of the next inert gas; the expected co-ordination number of four is observed in many complex salts, for example the neutral molecule $ZnCl_2(NH_3)_2$ and the ions $Cu(CN)_4^{3-}$, $GaCl_4^-$, HgI_4^{2-}. The same co-ordination number is shown by the Cu^{2+}, Ni^{2+} and Co^{2+} ions (with vacancies for nine, ten and eleven electrons, respectively), but the Fe^{2+} ion, and the similar Co^{3+} and Pt^{4+} ions, which can accommodate twelve electrons, form complexes with co-ordination number six, as do most of the transition metal ions with vacancies for more than twelve electrons. The Mo^{4+} and W^{4+} ions, with vacancies for sixteen electrons, however, do form 8:co-ordinated complex cyanides, $Mo(CN)_8^{4-}$ and $W(CN)_8^{4-}$.

In the first and second long periods ions of inert-gas structure require eighteen electrons to complete the next inert-gas structure. The large co-ordination number of nine is probably impossible for geometrical reasons and in the first long period these ions are usually 6:co-ordinate (as in TiF_6^{2-}); the larger ions in the second and third long periods sometimes have higher co-ordination numbers, e.g. ZrF_7^{3-}, TaF_8^{3-}.

Limitations of the Octet Theory

Whereas this simple electronic approach accounts for the co-ordination numbers of most of the common complex forming ions, it leaves unexplained the directive nature of the bonds; unless indeed this is regarded as a natural geometrical result of the mutual repulsion of the ligands. The peculiar, square-planar co-ordination observed in the complexes of the divalent ions of nickel, palladium, platinum and copper and of trivalent gold cannot, however, be explained geometrically; nor can the failure of the Ni^{2+}, Pd^{2+} and Pt^{2+} ions to form 5:co-ordinated complexes.

In addition to the 4:co-ordinated complexes, divalent nickel also forms a number of complexes with the co-ordination number six, for example the ammine $[Ni(NH_3)_6]^{2+}$. In these the number of donated electrons to be accommodated necessitates exceeding the next inert-gas structure on the nickel atom. The inert-gas structure is also exceeded in many 6:co-ordinated complexes of B subgroup elements, such as the ammines $[Zn(NH_3)_6]^{2+}$ and $[Cd(NH_3)_6]^{2+}$ and the complex halides $[GeCl_6]^{2-}$ and $[SnCl_6]^{2-}$. It must be realized, however, that this is already a common feature of the chemistry of the elements of the second short period, where 6:co-ordinated complexes include the oxalate $[Al(C_2O_4)_3]^{3-}$ and the fluorides $[SiF_6]^{2-}$ and $[PF_6]^{-}$ and even the neutral molecule of the gas SF_6.

It is thus apparent that although the co-ordination chemistry of some elements may be satisfactorily explained in terms of the completion of inert-gas structures and the attainment of particular "effective atomic numbers", this simple approach is inadequate to provide a whole picture of co-ordination chemistry.

THE VALENCY-BOND THEORY

In the Bohr atom the electrons are considered as occupying successive orbits at increasing distances from the atomic nucleus. In the quantum-mechanical description of the atom the electrons are placed in successive orbitals at increasing energy levels. These energy levels are defined by the quantum numbers, of which each electron in an atom has four:

(1) A principal quantum number, $n = 1, 2, 3, \ldots$, corresponding (at least for the lowest values of n) to an orbit in the Bohr atom.

(2) An azimuthal quantum number, $l = n-1, n-2, \ldots 0$, defining the angular momentum.

(3) A magnetic quantum number, $m = \pm l, \pm l-1, \pm l-2, \ldots 0$, representing the components of l in the direction of a magnetic field.

(4) A spin quantum number, $s = \pm\frac{1}{2}$.

	7p – – –		*5f* – – – – – – –	fourth long period.
7s –		*6d* – – – – –		
	6p – – –		*4f* – – – – – – –	third long period.
6s –		*5d* – – – – –		
	5p – – –			second long period.
5s –		*4d* – – – – –		
	4p – – –			first long period.
4s –		*3d* – – – – –		
	3p – – –			second short period.
3s –				
	2p – – –			first short period.
2s –				
1s –				H, He.

The energy differences due to the third and fourth quantum numbers are comparatively small and in the free gaseous atoms, electrons differing only in these quantum numbers are found to have equal energies. This levelling out of the small energy differences is referred to as degeneracy. A energy-level diagram can now be drawn showing successive energy levels, due only to variation of the first two quantum numbers. For convenience of reference the orbitals so obtained are labelled with the principal quantum number and a letter representing the second quantum number, thus:

$l = 0$, *s*-orbitals; one orbital, two electrons;
$l = 1$, *p*-orbitals; three orbitals, six electrons;
$l = 2$, *d*-orbitals; five orbitals, ten electrons;
$l = 3$, *f*-orbitals; seven orbitals, fourteen electrons.

Large increases in energy level are apparent after the accommodation of 2, 10, 18, 36, 54 or 86 electrons—corresponding to the structures of the inert gases. The difference in phase between the number of electrons with successive principal quantum numbers (2, 8, 18, 32, . . .) and the number of elements in successive periods (2, 8, 8, 18, 18, 32, . . .) is due to the overlap of the energy levels of the *d*- and *f*-orbitals with one principal quantum number with those of the *s*- and *p*-orbitals of the next or next but one.

Vector Properties and Hybrid Bond Orbitals

The most important orbitals involved in chemical bonding are the *s*- and *p*-orbitals; *d*-orbitals are also involved when more than four bonds are formed by the same atom, but there is no conclusive evidence of *f*-orbitals being involved in bond formation.

The *s*-orbitals have spherical symmetry: electrons in these orbitals produce spherically symmetrical regions of electron density, centred on the atomic nucleus. The *p*-orbitals, however, though spherically symmetrical as a group are not individually of spherical symmetry; electrons in these orbitals produce regions of electron density along cartesian axes originating at the atomic nucleus. If these *p*-orbitals are used in the formation of covalent bonds, the bound atoms will have to lie along these axes; that is to say, the bonds produced will be directed in space at angles

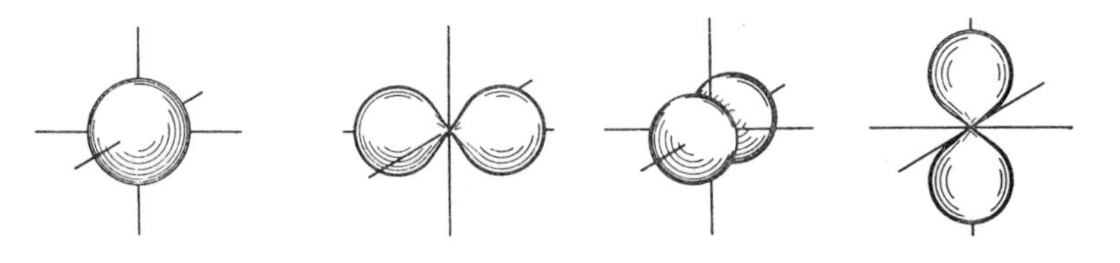

s-orbital Set of three *p*-orbitals

of 90° to one another. A bond angle of 92° is in fact observed in hydrogen sulphide, in which a reasonable electronic structure involves two of the *p*-orbitals of the sulphur atom in bonding:

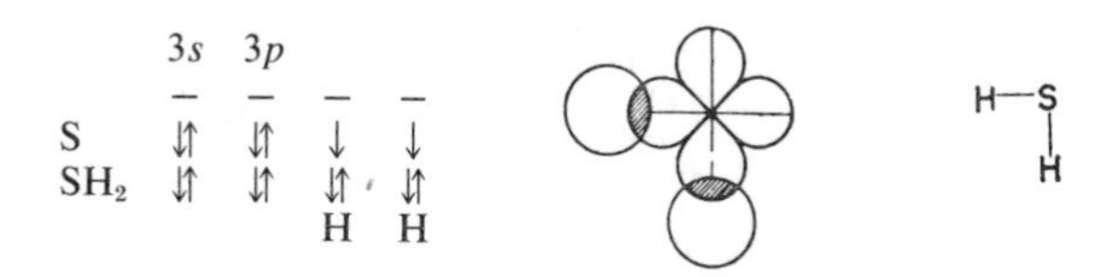

In the BX_3 compounds of boron the bonding is expected to involve one 2*s*- and two 2*p*-orbitals. This should lead to bond angles of 90° between two B—X bonds, the third bond (that involving the 2*s*-orbital) being indeterminate in direction, the most probable position being that which bisects the re-entrant angle between the other bonds. In fact, all BX_3 molecules have plane equilateral triangular structures with bond angles of 120°:

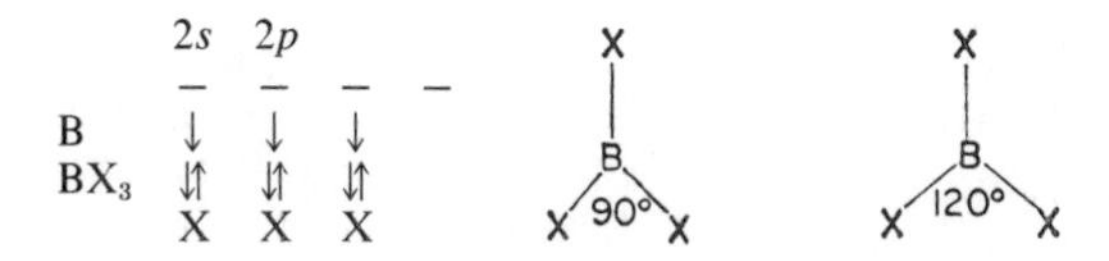

In the same way, the vector properties of the three 2*p*-orbitals and one 2*s*-orbital available would lead to a CX_4 molecule with three angles of 90°, whereas all CX_4 molecules are tetrahedral.

To account for these observations it is supposed that the electrons do not occupy ordinary atomic *s*- and *p*-orbitals, but that a new set of "hybrid-bond orbitals" is formed from the original atomic orbitals and that these impose a different stereochemistry. These "hybrid-bond orbital" systems are referred to by an appropriate combination of symbols, showing the atomic orbitals from which they are derived. Thus, the hybrid orbitals in the BX_3 molecules are referred to as a set of sp^2-orbitals and those in the CX_4 molecules as a set of sp^3-orbitals. The more common types of hybrid-bond orbitals and the stereochemistry imposed by them are as follows:

two *sp*-orbitals, linear X—M—X;
three sp^2-orbitals, plane equilateral triangular MX_3;
four sp^3-orbitals, tetrahedral MX_4;
six d^2sp^3-orbitals, octahedral MX_6;
four dsp^2-orbitals, square planar MX_4;
five dsp^3-orbitals, trigonal bipyramidal MX_5.

The tetrahedral configuration of the co-ordination compounds of the elements of the short periods and the B subgroups now appears as a natural consequence of the availability of one *s*-orbital and three *p*-orbitals of the acceptor cation. Octahedral co-ordination becomes possible only when there are also available two *d*-orbitals. This occurs in the d^6-ions of the transition metals (Fe^{2+}, Co^{3+}, Pt^{4+}), the available *d*-orbitals ($3d$) having a principal quantum number one less than the *s*- and *p*-orbitals ($4s$, $4p$); it also occurs in the second short period (SiF_6^{2-}, etc.), where the *d*-orbitals used ($3d$) have the same principal quantum number as the *s*- and *p*-orbitals ($3s$, $3p$). The square planar co-ordination characteristic of the d^8 ions, Ni^{2+}, Pd^{2+}, Pt^{2+} and Au^{3+}, arises as the result of the use in hybrid-bond formation of the one available *d*-orbital to produce a set of dsp^2-orbitals.

PARAMAGNETISM

The transition metals are distinguished from the metals of the short periods by their readiness to form cations without the loss of all their valency electrons. Thus the divalent cations typical of the transition metals of the first long period arise by the loss of the two $4s$-electrons, leaving a partly-filled group of $3d$-orbitals. According to Hund's principle of maximum multiplicity, the electrons in these orbitals remain, as far as possible, unpaired and with parallel spins.

Since atoms with unpaired electrons possess a permanent magnetic moment, many transition-metal compounds are paramagnetic, that is they tend to move into an applied magnetic field. The paramagnetic susceptibility due to uncompensated electron spins is given by:

$$\mu = \sqrt{[4S(S+1)]} \qquad (1)$$

where S is the sum of the spin quanta; and as each electron has a spin quantum of $\pm\frac{1}{2}$, this can be expressed as:

$$\mu = \sqrt{[n(n+2)]} \qquad (2)$$

where n is the number of electrons with uncompensated spins.

Experimentally the magnetic susceptibility, χ, is usually determined on a Gouy balance: this is an ordinary chemical balance, so arranged that the powdered or dissolved specimen can be hung below one of the balance pans in a small tube; the lower end of this tube lies between the poles of a powerful magnet and the upper end far enough from the poles of the magnet for the magnetic field to be comparatively insignificant. The specimen is weighed with and without the magnet in position and the molar paramagnetic susceptibility calculated from the equation:

$$\chi_M = \left(kv + \frac{2gv.dw}{AH^2}\right)\frac{M}{W} \qquad (3)$$

where k is the volume susceptibility of the medium, v the volume of the specimen, g the acceleration due to gravity, A the cross-sectional area of the specimen, H the magnetic field strength, W the weight of the specimen, dw the difference between the weighings and M its molecular weight.

As the susceptibility and the magnetic moment are related by the equation:

$$\chi_M = \frac{N^2\mu^2}{3RT}$$

the magnetic moment of the paramagnetic atom is given by:

$$\mu = \sqrt{(3RT\chi_M)}/N \qquad (4)$$

where N is Avogadro's number, and T the absolute temperature (though closer agreement with experimental results is observed if T is measured from an experimental zero, known as the Curie temperature).

In practice most transition metal compounds are "magnetically dilute", that is the atom with a permanent magnetic moment is surrounded by other atoms without any permanent moment. This prevents any possibility of interaction between neighbouring magnetic atoms, but as all atoms with paired electrons are slightly diamagnetic (i.e. tend to move out of a magnetic field), it is necessary to correct the experimentally determined susceptibility for the combined effect of the diamagnetism of all the atoms in the compound. This correction is comparatively small but may sometimes amount to about a quarter of the total so cannot be ignored. Replacement of χ_M in eqn. (4) by the corrected susceptibility, $\chi_{M'}$, now gives the "effective magnetic moment" of the paramagnetic atom:

$$\begin{aligned}\mu_{\text{eff}} &= \sqrt{(3RT\chi_{M'})}/N \\ &= 2{\cdot}84\sqrt{(T\chi_{M'})} \qquad (5)\end{aligned}$$

where the values of μ_{eff} in eqn. (5) are in Bohr magnetons (β) and correspond to those expected from eqn. (1) or (2). Table 1 shows expected and observed values of μ_{eff} for typical transition metal ions.

TABLE 1. THEORETICAL AND OBSERVED VALUES OF μ_{eff}

Cation	Electronic structure 3d					Unpaired electrons	μ_{eff} theory	μ_{eff} observed
V^{3+}	↓	↓				2	2·83	2·7–2·8
Cr^{3+}, Mn^{4+}	↓	↓	↓			3	3·88	3·7–3·9
Cr^{2+}, Mn^{3+}	↓	↓	↓	↓		4	4·90	4·8–4·9
Mn^{2+}, Fe^{3+}	↓	↓	↓	↓	↓	5	5·91	5·7–6·1
Fe^{2+}	⇃↾	↓	↓	↓	↓	4	4·90	5·1–5·5
Co^{2+}	⇃↾	⇃↾	↓	↓	↓	3	3·88	4·3–5·2
Ni^{2+}	⇃↾	⇃↾	⇃↾	↓	↓	2	2·83	2·9–3·2
Cu^{2+}	⇃↾	⇃↾	⇃↾	⇃↾	↓	1	1·73	1·8–2·0

Agreement between the expected and observed values is excellent for ions with one to five $3d$ electrons, but ions with six to nine $3d$ electrons give values significantly above those expected according to eqn. (1).

Where values of μ_{eff} differ from those expected, this is usually attributed to "orbital contribution". This is a contribution to the magnetic moment made by uncompensated magnetic quantum numbers. In a set of d-orbitals these may have values of ± 2, ± 1 or 0, so that a d^1-ion could have two quanta of orbital magnetic moment in addition to the spin moment; a d^2-ion could have $2+1=3$ quanta of orbital magnetic moment, and so on. In the same way as the spin quanta combine to give a magnetic moment according to eqn. (1), so the magnetic moment attributable to orbital contribution can be obtained from the equation

$$\mu = \sqrt{[L(L+1)]} \qquad (6)$$

The total magnetic moment of any paramagnetic ion is thus given by a combination of the spin and orbital contributions. These may interact with one another in a variety of ways, and no universally applicable rule can be given for calculating the total moment. In the transition metals of the first long period, however, the orbital contribution is always quite small, and observed moments differ only slightly from spin-only values, calculated from eqn. (1). This correspondence is often not so close in the second and third long periods and, in the lanthanide elements, where paramagnetism arises from an incomplete $4f$-shell, the orbital contribution is quite large.

Paramagnetism and Stereochemistry

Where the orbital contribution to the magnetic moment is significant, it is also sensitive to the stereochemical environment of the metal atom, and has been used for the diagnosis of stereochemistry. The most extensively studied example of this is provided by cobalt(II) which forms compounds with octahedral or tetrahedral stereochemistry. The spin-only moment for a d^7-ion is 3·88β and observed values fall in the range 4·3–4·7 for tetrahedral compounds and 4·6–5·2 for octahedral. Some typical values are shown in Table 2.

TABLE 2. MAGNETIC MOMENTS OF 4-METHYLPYRIDINE COMPLEXES OF COBALT(II) HALIDES (BOHR MAGNETONS)

Tetrahedral		Octahedral	
$CoI_2(4\text{-mepy})_2$	4·49	$CoI_2(4\text{-mepy})_4$	5·04
$CoBr_2(4\text{-mepy})_2$	4·41	$CoBr_2(4\text{-mepy})_4$	5·04
$CoCl_2(4\text{-mepy})_2$	4·48	$CoCl_2(4\text{-mepy})_4$	4·94

For a d^8-ion the spin only moment is 2·83β, but an orbital contribution of up to about 0·4β leads to observed moments in the range 2·9–3·3 for octahedral nickel(II) compounds. In this case, tetrahedral compounds have rather higher moments, ranging up to about 4β. Some values for typical nickel(II) complexes are shown in Table 3.

TABLE 3. MAGNETIC MOMENT AND STEREOCHEMISTRY OF SOME NICKEL(II) COMPLEXES

Compound	μ_{eff}	Stereochemistry
$Ni(NH_3)_6Cl_2$	3·11	octahedral
$Ni(en)_3SO_4$	3·16	octahedral
$Ni(sal)_2(H_2O)_2$†	3·15	octahedral
$Ni(DBM)_2py_2$†	3·03	octahedral
$(Ph_3AsCH_3)_2(NiCl_4)$	4·10	tetrahedral
$(N(C_2H_5)_4)_2NiBr_4$	3·87	tetrahedral

†sal = salicylaldehydato.
DBM = dibenzoylmethanato.

Attempts have also been made to correlate the magnetic moments and stereochemistry of copper(II) complexes, but in these compounds the orbital contribution is usually smaller, not often exceeding 0·3β, and values of magnetic moments are not accurate enough for any such classification to be of practical value.

As well as these comparatively small variations in orbital contribution, changes in the stereochemistry of a metal may also be accompanied by changes in the number of unpaired electrons, and so by relatively large changes in magnetic moment. The most familiar example is provided by nickel(II) complexes. In many of these complexes the nickel atom is surrounded by four donor atoms at the corners of a square, and the complexes are then diamagnetic; bis(dimethylglyoximato)nickel(II) is a very well-known example, and other examples are discussed in the next chapter.

The magnetic evidence shows that in these square-planar nickel(II) complexes, all the *d*-electrons are paired. The valency-bond approach explains this observation by the requirement for one of the *d*-orbitals to be available for bonding, square complexes being bound by dsp^2-hybrid-bond-orbitals:

	3*d*					4*s*	4*p*		
Ni^{2+}	⥮	⥮	⥮	↓	↓				
NiL_4	⥮	⥮	⥮	⥮	⥮	⥮	⥮	⥮	

A number of cobalt(II) complexes, with Schiff's bases and similar ligands, is also known with low magnetic moments. In this case, since a d^7-ion has an odd number of electrons, pairing of the *d*-electrons cannot lead to diamagnetism; but a moment of about 1·8β might be expected, corresponding to one unpaired electron. These compounds usually have moments of 2·4–2·8β, suggesting a rather large orbital contribution as in other cobalt(II) complexes, but their stereochemistry is not known, though it is commonly assumed that they are square-planar.

The requirement for some of the *d*-orbitals to be available for bonding may also occur in octahedral complexes; the non-bonding *d*-electrons must then be confined to the remaining *d*-orbitals, leading to reduced paramagnetism. Thus, in addition to the square complex $Ni(CN)_4^{2-}$, the octahedral, 6:co-ordinate complex cyanides of the ions, Fe^{2+}, Co^{3+} and Pt^{4+} are also diamagnetic and, in the $Fe(CN)_6^{3-}$ ion, the moment is reduced to 2·40β, corresponding to one unpaired electron.

	3*d*					4*s*	4*p*			
Fe^{2+}, Co^{3+}	⥮	↓	↓	↓	↓					
$[Fe(CN)_6]^{4-}$ / $[Co(CN)_6]^{3-}$	⥮	⥮	⥮	⥮ CN	⥮ CN	⥮ CN	⥮ CN	⥮ CN	⥮ CN	d^2sp^3 hybrid bonds
$[Fe(CN)_6]^{3-}$	⥮	⥮	↓	⥮ CN	⥮ CN	⥮ CN	⥮ CN	⥮ CN	⥮ CN	d^2sp^3-bonds, one unpaired electron
Ni^{2+}	⥮	⥮	⥮	↓	↓					
$[Ni(CN)_4]^{2-}$	⥮	⥮	⥮	⥮	⥮ CN	⥮ CN	⥮ CN	⥮ CN		dsp^2 hybrid bonds

In some circumstances the magnetic susceptibility provides useful evidence for the detailed structure of the compound concerned. Thus treatment of potassium ferrocyanide with nitric acid gives the deep red nitroprusside, $K_2[Fe(CN)_5(NO)]$, long considered to be a nitroso derivative of ferric iron. The nitroprussides, however, are diamagnetic and must be considered as derivatives of ferrous iron, the odd electron of the nitric oxide molecule having been transferred to the iron atom:

	3d					4s	4p		
$[Fe^{III}(CN)_5(NO)]^{2-}$	⇅	⇅	↓	⇅	⇅	⇅	⇅	⇅	⇅
				•NO	CN	CN	CN	CN	CN
$[Fe^{II}(CN)_5(NO^+)]^{2-}$	⇅	⇅	⇅	⇅	⇅	⇅	⇅	⇅	⇅
				NO	CN	CN	CN	CN	CN

Another example of the value of measurements of magnetic susceptibility is the demonstration of the double formula for hypophosphoric acid and its salts. The empirical formula, H_2PO_3, would lead to a paramagnetic molecule whereas the hypophosphates are diamagnetic.

The Magnetic Criterion of Bond Type: Inner- and Outer-orbital Complexes

Among the complex salts of iron and cobalt are some with abnormal magnetic properties. Thus the complex fluorides, $K_3[FeF_6]$ and $K_3[CoF_6]$, have high magnetic susceptibilities, corresponding to the presence of five and four unpaired electrons, respectively, as in the free metal cations. Pauling explained these high numbers of unpaired electrons by suggesting that in these complexes the Fe—F and Co—F bonds were electrostatic, not covalent as in most complex salts. In this way it is possible to use magnetic properties as a criterion of bond type, so long as the free metal cation has from four to seven electrons in the *d*-shell; with less than four or more than seven *d*-electrons there is no distinction in the magnetic properties between the covalent and ionic complexes.

This idea that the bonds in the complex ion are ionic does not accord well with the familiar suppression of ferric ion concentration produced by fluorides (for example, the decolorization of ferric thiocyanate solutions), nor with the properties of the ferrioxalates, which also have high magnetic susceptibilities: the ferrioxalates can be resolved into optical isomers and show the absorption band in the infrared at 1730 cm^{-1}, characteristic of carboxyl groups in esters. The ferrioxalates, however, are markedly more reactive than the diamagnetic (and therefore "covalent") cobaltioxalates, rhodioxalates and iridioxalates: these diamagnetic complexes are highly resistant to hydrolysis, ferrioxalates are rapidly hydrolysed, even by boiling water; the racemization of the optical isomers of the diamagnetic oxalates is very slow, that of ferrioxalates rapid in dilute solutions of alkali oxalates; ferrioxalates exchange rapidly in solution with radioactive oxalate ions, cobaltioxalates at an immeasurably slow rate.

This conflict between the magnetic and other evidence may be resolved by the suggestion that in the complexes with high magnetic susceptibilities the bonding is covalent, but involves the outer *d*-orbitals (4*d*) of the iron or cobalt atom, leaving the maximum number of unpaired electrons in the inner (3*d*) orbitals. In this case the hybrid bond orbitals are derived from the 4*s*-, 4*p*- and 4*d*-atomic orbitals, instead of the usual 4*s*-, 4*p*- and 3*d*-atomic orbitals:

	3*d*					4*s*	4*p*			4*d*					
Fe^{3+}	↓	↓	↓	↓	↓										
$[Fe(CN)_6]^{3-}$	⇅	⇅	↓	⇅	⇅	⇅	⇅	⇅	⇅						"inner-
				CN	CN	CN	CN	CN	CN						orbital"
$[FeF_6]^{3-}$ or $[Fe(Ox)_3]^{3-}$	↓	↓	↓	↓	↓	⇅	⇅	⇅	⇅	⇅	⇅				"outer-
						X	X	X	X	X	X				orbital"
Co^{3+}	⇅	↓	↓	↓	↓										
$[CoF_6]^{3-}$	⇅	↓	↓	↓	↓	⇅	⇅	⇅	⇅	⇅	⇅				"outer-
						F	F	F	F	F	F				orbital"
$[Co(Ox)_3]^{3-}$ $[Co(NH_3)_6]^{3+}$	⇅	⇅	⇅	⇅	⇅	⇅	⇅	⇅	⇅						"inner-
				X	X	X	X	X	X						orbital"

This method of resolving the conflict was considered by Pauling, but rejected by him on the grounds that the extra energy required to bring into use the outer *d*-orbitals was too great. That "outer-orbital" bond hybridization is permissible, however, can be seen from the formation of 6:co-ordinated complexes of zinc and cadmium (for example, the ammines $[M(NH_3)_6]^{2+}$), and the formation of clearly covalent compounds such as SF_6 by elements in the second short period. In this respect, it is interesting that the complex oxalates of aluminium, $[Al(C_2O_4)_3]^{3-}$, in which there is no alternative to "outer-orbital" bonding ($3s$, $3p^3$, $3d^2$), show the characteristic infrared absorption at 1730 cm^{-1}, and resemble the ferrioxalates in being readily hydrolysed, rapidly racemized and undergoing rapid exchange with labelled oxalate ions.

Conversely, the chromioxalates, for which magnetic evidence is of no value (Cr^{3+} is a $3d^3$-ion), resemble the cobaltioxalates in general lack of reactivity and presumably have "inner-orbital" bond hybridization.

Amongst the diamagnetic "inner-orbital" complexes of trivalent cobalt is the hydrate, which must thus be considered a true co-ordination compound $[Co(OH_2)_6]^{3+}$. There is much other evidence that water of hydration of the transition metal cations is in fact co-ordinated, for example the isomerism in the chromic chloride hydrates (p. 10) and the square-planar location of the molecules of water in hydrated cupric salts (p. 67). Thus it is now widely accepted that the high magnetic susceptibilities in aqueous solution of all the transition metal cations of the first long period, except Co^{3+}, are due to the presence of these ions in the form of 6:co-ordinated complex hydrates, with "outer-orbital" bond hybridization and it is doubtful whether any cases are known of these ions occurring in the "free" state, even in anhydrous crystals.

Antiferromagnetism

In some transition metal compounds the paramagnetic atoms are close enough together for interaction to occur. It may then happen that, due to the proximity of the paramagnetic centres, new energy levels may become available in which the electrons can be paired up, thus lowering the magnetic moment. An example of this occurs in the nickel(II) fluoride complex $KNiF_3$; the spin-only value of the moment would be $2{\cdot}83\beta$, but the observed value is only $2{\cdot}1\beta$. If the neighbouring nickel atoms are separated by isomorphous incorporation of zinc into the crystal, the moment rises to $2{\cdot}8\beta$ as expected. Many transition metal oxides and halides, in which the low ratio of non-metal atoms to metal atoms inevitably leads to proximity of the metal atoms to one another, have low moments.

In some cases, transition metal compounds form molecules in which two or more paramagnetic centres are close together, but their interaction is restricted to the molecule, and does not continue throughout the whole crystal. The most familiar example of this is copper(II) acetate, which crystallizes as molecules with the formula $Cu_2(CH_3CO_2)_4(H_2O)_2$, in which the two copper atoms are about the same distance apart as in metallic copper (XXXIV, p. 69). A new energy level is made available in which the odd electrons can be paired; however, this level is only very slightly lower than those occupied by the unpaired electrons, so the actual state of the molecule is a mixture of the diamagnetic and paramagnetic states and, at room temperature, has a magnetic moment of $1{\cdot}4\beta$ per copper atom.

The population of the two states varies with temperature so that the moment per copper atom rises to about $1{\cdot}6\beta$ at 130°C, and falls to $0{\cdot}4\beta$ at −180°C (Fig. 1).

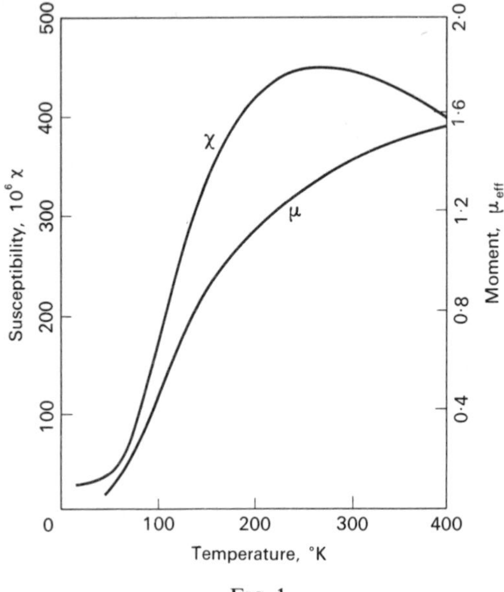

FIG. 1

Variation of the magnetic moment with temperature in this way can only be expected when the separation of the diamagnetic and paramagnetic energy levels is of the same order of magnitude as the thermal energy of the system kT. In copper(II) acetate the energy separation is about 0·9 kcal/mole, but in the corresponding chromium(II) compound, which has the same structure, the energy separation must be considerably greater, as this compound is diamagnetic at room temperature.

Most other compounds which show antiferromagnetic behaviour are more complicated than copper(II) acetate, in that the molecule in which antiferromagnetic interaction occurs contains more than two paramagnetic centres. Examples of this type include the acetates of iron(III) and chromium(III) and the "cluster" compounds, the structures of which are described in the next chapter.

THE CRYSTAL-FIELD THEORY

Despite the success of the valence-bond theory in interpreting the main features of co-ordination chemistry and providing an explanation for paramagnetism, there are a number of aspects which it has been unable to treat successfully.

Outstanding among the properties of transition metals which the valence-bond theory does not explain is the occurrence of coloured compounds. We may also note the behaviour of the d^8-ions Ni^{2+}, Pd^{2+},

Pt^{2+} and Au^{3+}, which rarely form the 5:co-ordinate complexes which might be expected. The valence-bond theory is able to propose a form of bond hybridization suitable for the square-planar complexes commonly formed by these ions, but this does not explain why this structure is preferred to other possible stereochemical configurations, such as tetrahedral or 5:co-ordinate trigonal-bipyramidal. The necessity to "promote" one $3d$-electron to some higher energy level, so that dsp^2 hybridization can occur in square-planar copper(II) complexes, is another weakness, and the valence-bond theory offers no explanation as to why "outer-orbital" bonding is preferred in some compounds.

Another approach, based on theoretical work on the interaction of ions in crystals by Bethe (1929) and van Vleck (1931–1935), and known as the crystal-field theory, has proved remarkably successful in explaining some of these problems. The crystal-field theory is an electrostatic approach, regarding a complex as consisting of a central cation surrounded by a cage of anions (or the negative ends of ligand molecules). The theory is concerned primarily with the effect of this environment on the energies of the d-orbitals of the metal atom.

The Effect of the Ligand Field on the d-orbitals

The d-orbitals differ from the p-orbitals in not being all alike: three of these orbitals (the d_{xy}, d_{xz} and d_{yz}) resemble one another in producing regions of electron density in the three planes of cartesian axes, but directed between these axes:

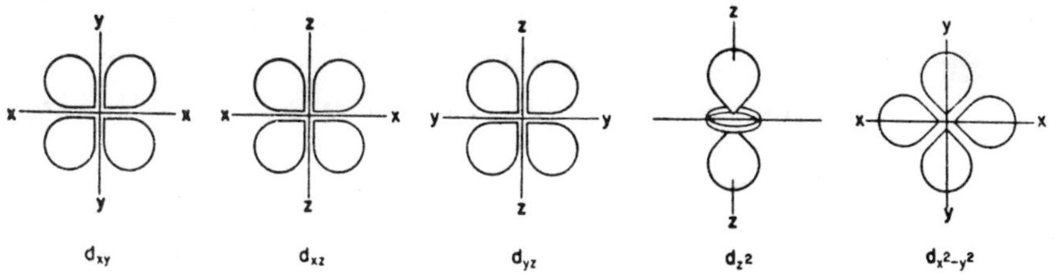

d_{xy} d_{xz} d_{yz} d_{z^2} $d_{x^2-y^2}$

The other two differ from these three and from one another: the $d_{x^2-y^2}$-orbital produces regions of electron density along the x- and y-axes; the d_{z^2}-orbital produces most of its electron density along the z-axis, with a small proportion in the form of an annulus in the xy-plane. The d_{xy}-, d_{xz}- and d_{yz}-orbitals together form a set with spherical symmetry and the $d_{x^2-y^2}$ and d_{z^2} together form another set with spherical symmetry, but these two sets of orbitals are affected differently by their environment.

In an octahedral complex ligands lie along the x-, y- and z-axes. The electrostatic repulsion between these ligands and the electrons of the central cation will be much greater if these electrons are in the $d_{x^2-y^2}$

or d_{z^2}-orbitals than if they are in the d_{xy}-, d_{xz}- or d_{yz}-orbitals; hence the d-orbitals, which are degenerate (i.e. all of equal energy) in the "free" ion are split into two groups, the energy of the $d_{x^2-y^2}$- and d_{z^2}-orbitals being increased far more by the presence of ligands lying along the axes on which these orbitals produce their regions of maximum electron density.

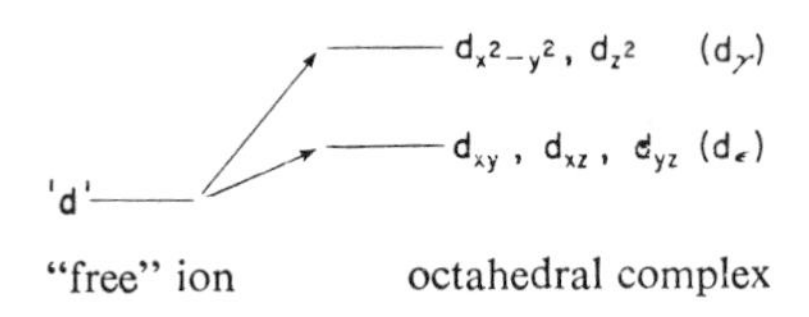

In a tetrahedral complex, it is the d_{xy}-, d_{xz}-, and d_{yz}-orbitals which produce their regions of maximum electron density in the direction nearest the ligands, and the above splitting of the d-orbitals is reversed.

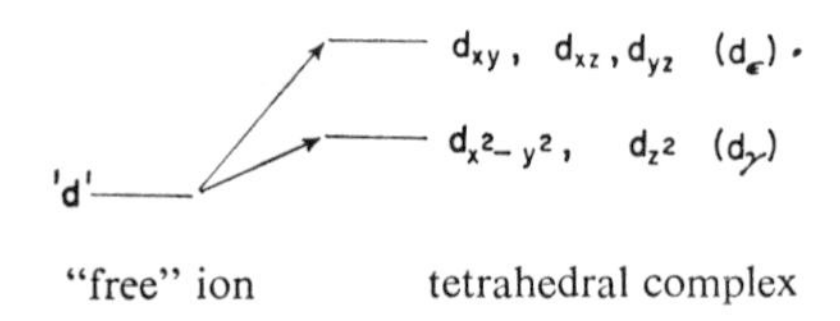

In the above diagrams the overall increase in the energy level of the d-orbitals is emphasized as well as their splitting, but it has become conventional to draw such diagrams with a new arbitrarily chosen energy level for the degenerate d-orbitals in the free ion. The two diagrams below show the energies of the upper and lower d-orbitals relative to the arbitrary zero and the orbital separation energy Δ.

d_γ
$0{\cdot}6\,\Delta$
$0{\cdot}4\,\Delta$
d_ε
d_ε
$0{\cdot}4\,\Delta$
$0{\cdot}6\,\Delta$
d_γ

Gaseous ion | Octahedral field | Tetrahedral field

Several different nomenclatures have been proposed for these different energy levels; that which will be used here refers to the d_{xy}, d_{xz} and d_{yz} orbitals as d_ϵ (other usages are t_{2g} and γ_5) and the $d_{x^2-y^2}$ and d_{z^2} orbitals as d_γ (other usages are e_g and γ_3). The orbital separation energy Δ is often represented as $10D_q$.

Although the effect of an octahedral or tetrahedral environment is to split the d-orbital energy levels into two new levels, other stereochemical arrangements can be expected to produce a more complex splitting. The only other stereochemistry which is common in transition metals is the tetragonal or square-planar configuration observed in complexes of d^8- and d^9-ions. In this case, if the x- and y-axes are taken in the plane of the ligands and in between them (very many such compounds contain bidentate ligands and the molecular symmetry axes then lie between the donor atoms, not towards them) the d-orbitals can be expected to be split into four levels, as follows:

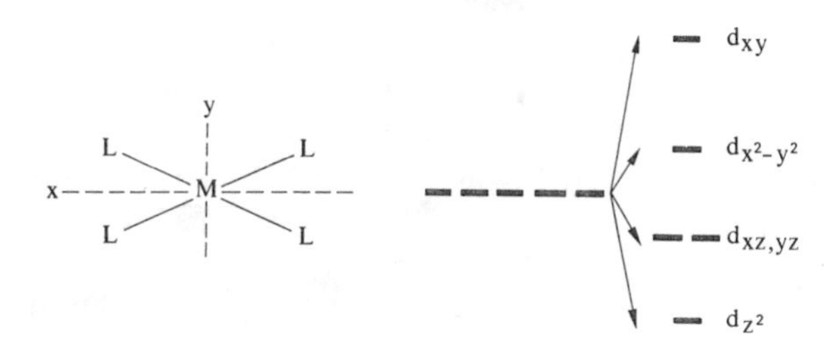

Absorption Spectra

One of the results of the comparatively small energy difference between the subdivided d-orbitals is that electronic transitions from the lower group to the higher can be brought about by the absorption of visible light. This leads to the complex compounds appearing coloured. Observation of the frequency of the absorbed light and application of the Einstein equation relating frequency and energy:

$$E = Nh\nu$$

is the most satisfactory method of determining the energy separation between the sets of d-orbitals.

Absorption spectra arising from such transitions consist of a series of symmetrical absorption bands, each of which can be defined by three parameters (Fig. 2).

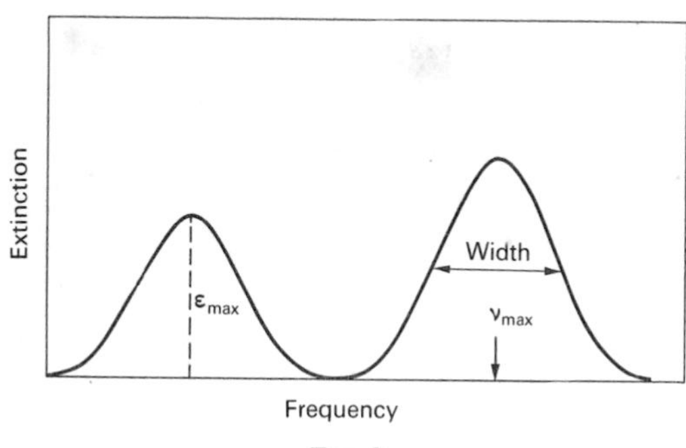

FIG. 2

(1) the wavelength or frequency of maximum intensity, λ_{max} or ν_{max};
(2) the extinction, ϵ;
(3) the width (measured at half the height of the band).

The frequency ν_{max} corresponds to the energy of the electronic transition; in the simplest case it would correspond to the orbital separation energy. The extinction, ϵ, represents the probability of the transition taking place; since all $d \rightarrow d$ transitions are symmetry forbidden, ϵ is small. These transitions probably become possible as a result of the lowering of molecular symmetry by internal vibrations. As a general rule, extinctions are much higher in tetrahedral complexes (ϵ up to 1000) than in octahedral ($\epsilon < 50$). When transitions can be observed which are spin-forbidden, as well as symmetry-forbidden, the extinctions are still lower ($\epsilon < 1$).

The width of the absorption bands arises from the superimposing of vibrational energies. In transition metals the absorption bands commonly have widths of the order of 0·2–0·5μ^{-1} (2000–5000 cm^{-1}, 6–15 kcal/mole); but when transitions occur between the much better shielded *f*-orbitals (in lanthanide ions) the absorption bands are much narrower.

Crystal-field theory provides an explanation for the occurrence of these spectra, and accounts for the energies of observed absorption bands in the following way.

Ligand-field Spectra

If the ligands in a complex are considered as producing a group of point charges in the directions of the donor atoms, the orbital separation energy will increase as these charges increase. The group of point charges

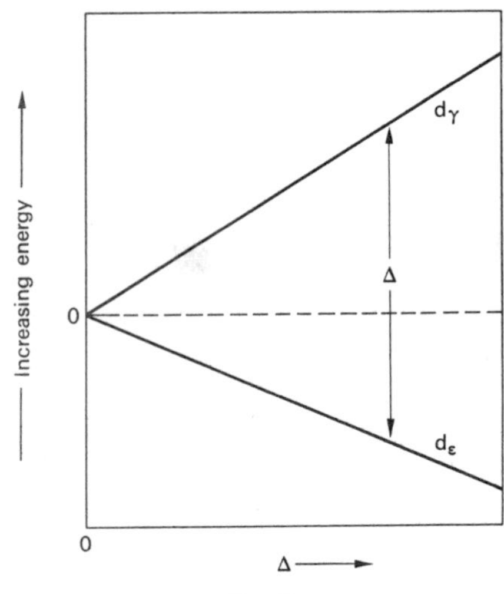

FIG. 3

constitutes a "ligand field", and Fig. 3 shows the effect of increasing ligand field on d-orbital separation energy in an octahedral complex. This behaviour is illustrated by the Ti^{3+} ion, which has a d^1-structure. In aqueous solution this ion can be considered as an octahedral complex $[Ti(H_2O)_6]^{3+}$ ion. The solution has an absorption band with maximum intensity at 500 mμ, equivalent to a transition energy of 60 kcal/mole. The transition concerned can be represented thus:

		d_ϵ			d_γ
	—	—	—	—	—
Ti^{3+}	↓				
↓					
$*Ti^{3+}$				↓	

Another example, almost as simple as this, is provided by the d^9-ion, Cu^{2+}. In this case, too, there is only one possible transition:

		d_ϵ			d_γ
	—	—	—	—	—
Cu^{2+}	⇃↾	⇃↾	⇃↾	⇃↾	↓
↓					
$*Cu^{2+}$	⇃↾	⇃↾	↓	⇃↾	⇃↾

and the absorption spectrum of the Cu^{2+} ion in aqueous solution also shows a single absorption band, at 800 mμ (Fig. 4).

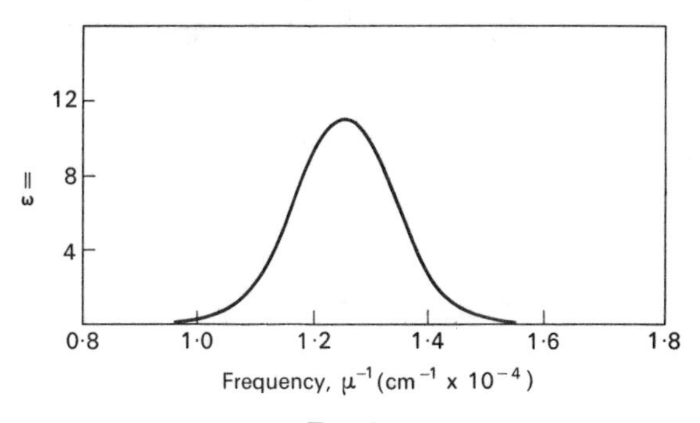

FIG. 4

Since the splitting of the d-orbitals is produced by the ligands, the orbital separation energy can be expected to be ligand dependent, and Table 4 gives some data for copper(II) complexes of the type CuL_4 in aqueous solution, where two water molecules are presumed to complete the octahedral environment of the metal atom.

TABLE 4. WAVELENGTH AND ENERGY OF $d \rightarrow d$ TRANSITION IN AQUEOUS SOLUTIONS OF COPPER(II) COMPLEXES

Complex	Wavelength (mμ)	Energy (kcal/mole)
$Cu(H_2O)_4^{2+}$	800	37·5
$Cu(C_2O_4)_2^{2-}$	700	43·0
$Cu(NH_2CH_2CO_2^-)_2$	620	48·5
$Cu(NH_3)_4^{2+}$	590	51·0
$Cu(C_5H_5N)_4^{2+}$	590	51·0
$Cu(NH_2CH_2CH_2NH_2)_2^{2+}$	545	55·0

The d^1- and d^9-ions are the only ones which give such simple energy diagrams as Fig. 2. In all other cases the energy diagrams are much more complicated. The reasons for this are as follows:

(1) When there are two to eight d-electrons, various combinations of paired and unpaired electrons are possible. Different combinations can be observed by differences in magnetic moment. When listing the different possibilities, this is done in spectroscopic nomenclature by the "multiplicity", the value of $2S+1$, where $S = \Sigma s$, the sum of the uncompensated spin quanta. Table 5 gives the values of multiplicity due to various numbers of uncompensated electron spins.

TABLE 5. MULTIPLICITY AND NUMBER OF UNPAIRED ELECTRONS

Number unpaired	0	1	2	3	4	5
$2S+1$	1	2	3	4	5	6
$\mu_{eff}(\beta)$	0	1·73	2·83	3·88	4·90	5·91

(2) For each multiplicity there may be several possible values for the total orbital magnetic moment, $L = \Sigma l$, where l is the magnetic quantum number of each occupied orbital. In listing possible states of the atom, values of L are represented by capital letters, thus:

$L = \Sigma l =$	0	1	2	3	4	5
represented	S	P	D	F	G	H

The combination of L and the multiplicity is shown by the capital letter representing L with the multiplicity as a superscript prefix. Thus, in the Ti^{3+} ion mentioned above, which has a d^1-structure, there is one unpaired electron, which will occupy the orbital of magnetic quantum number +2, so the state of the ion in spectroscopic nomenclature is ^2D. The possible states of other ions can be worked out similarly. For a d^2-ion, for example, the lowest energy possibilities are as follows, the magnetic quantum numbers being placed above each $3d$-orbital.

+2	+1	0	−1	−2	
↓	↓				^3F
↓			↓		^3P
⇃↾					^1G
	⇃↾				^1D
		⇃↾			^1S

(3) When there are several states possible for the ion in the absence of any ligand field, each of these states will be split in a different way by a ligand field. Figure 5 shows the effect of increasing octahedral ligand field on the energy levels of the Ni^{2+} ion; this ion has a d^8-structure, and gives rise to the same spectroscopic states as the d^2-ion.

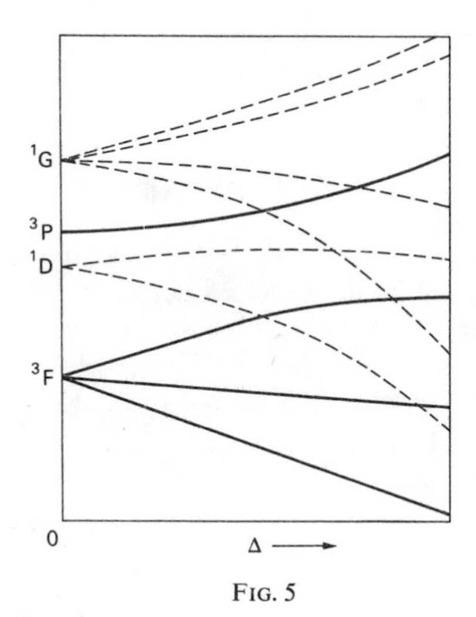

FIG. 5

Transitions between the four triplet states are spin allowed, but symmetry forbidden, and can be expected to give rise to three absorption bands. In practice, these bands are observed near 1000, 600 and 400 mμ, and have extinction coefficients in the range 1–20. Typical values for some nickel(II) complexes are shown in Table 6.

TABLE 6. ABSORPTION BANDS OF Ni^{2+} COMPLEXES OF HIGH-SPIN (TRIPLET STATE)

Complex	Transition energies (kcal/mole)		
$Ni(H_2O)_6^{2+}$	29	45	75
$Ni(NH_2CH_2CO_2^-)_3$	33	50	82
$Ni(NH_3)_6^{2+}$	34	53	84
$Ni(NH_2CH_2CH_2NH_2)_3^{2+}$	35	57	88

Transitions between the triplet and singlet states are spin-forbidden and so low in intensity that they cannot be observed, unless small humps in the absorption curves, which are often observed between the main absorption bands, are assigned to these transitions (Fig. 6).

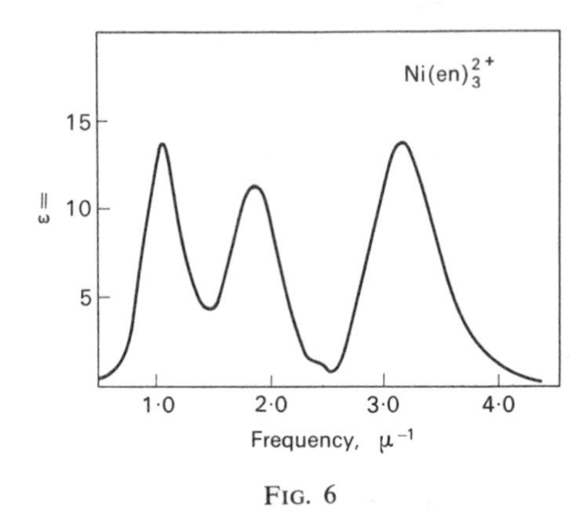

FIG. 6

In Fig. 5 the dotted lines show the effect which an octahedral ligand field could be expected to have on the singlet states of a Ni^{2+} ion. Almost all known diamagnetic nickel(II) compounds, however, have square-planar stereochemistry, and rather different splittings could then be expected. In practice, electronic transitions in these complexes occur in the ultraviolet region, and are usually obscured by charge-transfer spectra.

Charge-transfer Spectra

Charge-transfer spectra are due to electronic transitions between orbitals common to both metal and ligand atoms; or in terms of atomic orbitals, to transitions which involve electron transfer from metal to ligand or vice versa:

$$M+L \rightarrow M^{+}+L^{-}$$

or

$$M+L \rightarrow M^{-}+L^{+}$$

Absorption bands of this type are of high intensity ($\epsilon \sim 10{,}000$). Some examples for a series of iron(III) complexes are shown in Fig. 7.

While the absorption spectra of iron(III) complexes show charge-transfer bands in some cases far into the visible region of the spectrum, absorption bands of this type are more often confined to the ultraviolet.

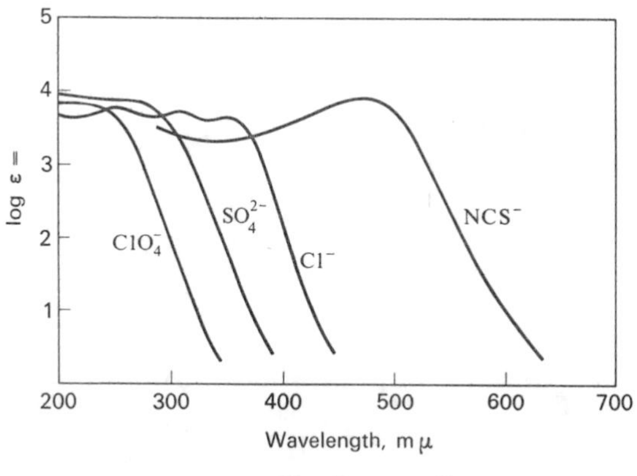

FIG. 7

The position of charge-transfer bands appears to depend on the polarizability of the ligand and on the nature of the metal atom. Ligands which are attached by highly polarizable donor atoms such as sulphur or phosphorus, frequently produce charge-transfer bands well into the visible region, and these may largely obscure the ligand-field bands characteristic of the transition metal ion.

The Spectrochemical Series

The effect of ligand fields on the splitting of *d*-orbital energy levels results in absorption spectra which are characteristic for each transition metal cation and for each stereochemistry of the cation. The appearance of a particular pattern of absorption bands thus provides evidence of the stereochemistry of transition metal ions in solution which could not be obtained by any other method.

However, although a pattern of absorption bands is characteristic of each cation and its stereochemistry, the exact position of the bands depends upon the ligand field, and so varies from ligand to ligand. As a result of accumulating spectroscopic data for complexes with many different metals it has become apparent that the relative ligand fields produced by different ligands are independent of the metal. Ligands can thus be arranged in order of increasing ligand field, and the same order holds for all metals, though the actual ligand fields produced vary from metal to metal. This list of ligands, arranged in order of increasing ligand field produced, is known as the spectrochemical series, and a shortened version of the series is as follows:

$$I^- < Br^- < Cl^- < F^- < OH^- < RCO_2^- < H_2O < NCS^- < NH_3 \sim py < en < dipy < o\text{-phen} < CN^-.$$

Tables 4 and 6 give some idea of the sort of shift in the position of absorption bands which occurs in complexes of the ions Cu^{2+} and Ni^{2+}. Table 7 gives some data for the two bands in the visible region which are characteristic of octahedral, diamagnetic Co^{3+} complexes; these bands have extinctions between 50 and 200.

TABLE 7. ABSORPTION BANDS OF DIAMAGNETIC COMPLEXES OF Co^{3+}

Complex	Wavelengths (mμ)		Energies (kcal/mole)	
$[Co(C_2O_4)_3]^{3-}$	606	435	49·5	69·0
$[Co(NH_3)_5Cl]^{2+}$	525	365	57·3	82·4
$[Co(NH_3)_5(OH)]^{2+}$	515	385†	59·3	78·0†
$[Co(NH_3)_5(CO_3)]^{+}$	515	378†	58·3	79·5†
$[Co(NH_3)_5(NO_3)]^{2+}$	500	358	60·0	83·9
$[Co(NH_3)_5(NCS)]^{2+}$	490	310†	61·2	97·0†
$[Co(NH_3)_6]^{3+}$	480	345	62·6	86·9
$[Co(NH_2CH_2CH_2NH_2)_3]^{3+}$	470	342	63·9	87·8
$[Co(CN)_6]^{3-}$	320	260	94·0	115·4

†Shoulders on absorption curve.

High-spin and Low-spin Complexes

When a transition metal ion in an octahedral complex contains four, five, six or seven *d*-electrons, alternative configurations are possible, which differ in spin multiplicity. Table 8 shows these alternatives and also corresponding unique configurations for d^3 and d^8-ions.

TABLE 8. ALTERNATIVE CONFIGURATIONS OF TRANSITION METAL IONS

Total *d*-electrons	Typical ion	Low-spin form d_ϵ			Low-spin form d_γ		No. odd	High-spin form d_ϵ			High-spin form d_γ		No. odd
		–	–	–	–	–		–	–	–	–	–	
3	Cr^{3+}	↓	↓	↓			3	↓	↓	↓	↓		3
4	Mn^{3+}	↓↑	↓	↓			2	↓	↓	↓	↓		4
5	Fe^{3+}	↓↑	↓↑	↓			1	↓	↓	↓	↓	↓	5
6	Co^{3+}	↓↑	↓↑	↓↑			0	↓↑	↓	↓	↓	↓	4
7	Co^{2+}	↓↑	↓↑	↓↑	↓		1	↓↑	↓↑	↓	↓	↓	3
8	Ni^{2+}	↓↑	↓↑	↓↑	↓	↓	2	↓↑	↓↑	↓↑	↓	↓	2

The configuration adopted in any particular compound is determined by the relative magnitudes of the orbital separation energy Δ and the spin-pairing energy Π. The spin-pairing energy Π is not much affected by changes of ligand, and is of the same order of magnitude in the 3*d*-, 4*d*- and 5*d*-orbitals; it can be obtained experimentally from atomic spectra. The orbital separation energy Δ can be obtained from absorption spectra and increases in magnitude as the position of the ligand in the spectrochemical series moves from left to right. Table 9 gives some values of Δ and Π for aqueous solutions of transition metal cations, in which the ion is presumed to exist as the complex hydrate $[M(H_2O)_6]^+$.

TABLE 9. ORBITAL SEPARATION AND SPIN-PAIRING ENERGIES FOR IONS M^{2+} AND M^{3+} IN AQUEOUS SOLUTIONS

No. of *d*-electrons	Ion M^{2+}	Δ	Π	Ion M^{3+}	Δ	Π
4	Cr^{2+}	41	69	Mn^{3+}	61	80
5	Mn^{2+}	23	75	Fe^{3+}	40	84
6	Fe^{2+}	30	51	Co^{3+}	52	60
7	Co^{2+}	27	66			

In every case Π is greater than Δ, and consequently, the high-spin configuration can be expected. This configuration is in fact observed in every case except Co^{3+}, for which the difference between Δ and Π is quite small. The $[Co(H_2O)_6]^{3+}$ ion must lie very near the point at which the electronic configuration changes as the complex ion $[CoF_6]^{3-}$ and even the neutral compound $CoF_3.3H_2O$ have the high-spin configuration, though the ligand field produced by fluoride ions is only slightly less than that produced by water molecules.

Replacement of water by ligands further to the right in the spectrochemical series raises the ligand field, and will eventually cause spin pairing when Δ becomes greater than Π. When Δ and Π are only slightly different in the hydrates this change can be expected with ligands only slightly to the right of water in the series, but when, as in the $[Fe(H_2O)_6]^{3+}$ ion, Π is much greater than Δ, the only complexes which can be expected to have the low-spin configuration are those with ligands on the far right of the series; it is thus found that, whereas the only cobalt(III) complexes which have the high-spin configuration are the fluorides, all iron(III) complexes have the high-spin configuration except those with cyanide, dipyridyl, phenanthroline and related ligands.

In the second and third transition series, much larger values of Δ are observed, and this is reflected in the low-spin configuration of almost all complexes of these elements.

It is interesting to compare the valence-bond and ligand-field interpretations of observed differences in magnetic properties. In the valence-bond treatment spin pairing is brought about because some of the *d*-orbitals are required for "inner-orbital" bonding; it is the nature of the bonding which determines the *d*-electron distribution. In the crystal-field treatment, spin pairing is brought about by the environment, no reference being made to bonding. Once the electrons have been forced into the low-spin configuration, some inner *d*-orbitals may become available for bonding, but the crystal-field approach is not concerned with this aspect.

THE SIDGWICK–POWELL THEORY

The simple MX_3 and MX_2 molecules of groups V and VI have permanent dipole moments indicating not only the polarity of the bonds but also the non-planarity or non-linearity of the molecules as a whole. The simplest explanation of this is that only the *p*-orbitals are involved in the bonding, leading to bond angles of about 90°, as observed in some of the hydrides, e.g.:

$$NH_3, 107°; PH_3, 94°; AsH_3, 92°; SbH_3, 91°; OH_2, 104°; SH_2, 92°$$

the higher bond angles in ammonia and water being attributed to repulsion of the hydrogen atoms attached to the small oxygen or nitrogen atoms.

In 1940, however, Sidgwick and Powell pointed out that the stereochemistry of many molecules having non-bonding pairs of electrons could be explained on the assumption that *all* the electrons on the atom combined to form a set of hybrid-bond orbitals, only some of which were used for bonding; that is that the non-bonding pairs of electrons were also involved in the bond hybridization. In this case the MX_3 molecules of group V should be pyramidal, with bond angles of 109·5°. This idea is supported by the bond angles in NF_3 (102°) and $N(CH_3)_3$ (108°), which should be larger than those in ammonia if the bond angle of 107° is the result of mutual repulsion of the hydrogen atoms.

The decreasing bond angle in the series NH_3, PH_3, AsH_3, SbH_3 is now explained in terms of the repulsion of the bonding electrons (not the bound atoms), which will be closer to the central atom when this has a higher electronegativity; replacement of the hydrogen atoms of ammonia by fluorine atoms would withdraw the bonding electrons from the nitrogen atom, thus allowing the bond angle to become smaller.

There are a number of molecules with non-bonding electrons in which the octet is exceeded on the central atom and the Sidgwick–Powell theory is particularly successful in accounting for the stereochemistry of these. Thus, the peculiarly distorted tetrahedral structures of the tetrahalides of selenium and tellurium are derived from the trigonal bipyramidal configuration enforced by dsp^3-hybridization, one of the equatorial pairs of electrons being non-bonding. The T-shaped molecule of chlorine trifluoride is similarly derived from a trigonal bipyramid with two vacant equatorial positions:

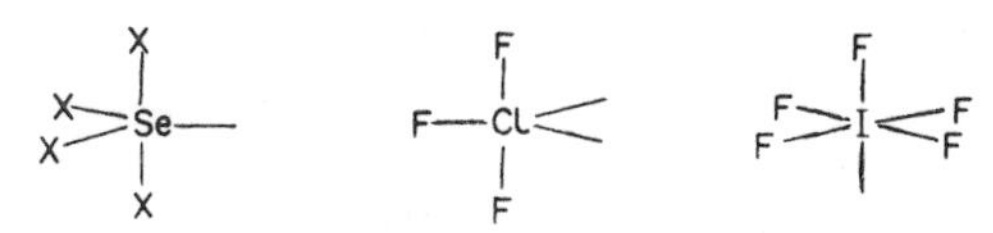

The unusual square-pyramidal molecule of iodine pentafluoride can also be seen to derive from an octahedral arrangement of the six electron pairs on the iodine atom, five of which are bonding and one non-bonding; the planar dimeric molecule I_2Cl_6 is similarly obtained from iodine atoms each of which has four bonding and two non-bonding electron pairs. Closely related to the interhalogen compounds are the fluorides of xenon and krypton, and the structures of these can be interpreted the same way.

Oxygen Compounds

The Sidgwick–Powell approach can be applied to molecular oxides and oxy-acid anions if these are treated as co-ordination compounds in which O^{2-} ions are co-ordinated to positive cations by single bonds; any double bonding which may occur is then found not to affect the already determined stereochemistry.

Thus the isoelectronic series of ions SiO_4^{4-}, PO_4^{3-}, SO_4^{2-} and ClO_4^- can be expected to be tetrahedral if they are regarded as co-ordination compounds of four O^{2-} ions with central inert gas ions Si^{4+}, P^{5+}, S^{6+} and Cl^{7+}: as a result of co-ordination, each cation acquires four electron pairs, which will be arranged tetrahedrally, and will determine the stereochemistry of the complex anion. If this approach is adopted in treating the molecules and ions of MO_3 and MO_2 types, it provides a satisfactory interpretation of their stereochemistry: the molecule SO_3 is treated as a co-ordination compound of three O^{2-} ions with an inert-gas S^{6+} ion, which thus acquires a sextet of electrons leading to the observed plane triangular molecule; on the other hand, the isoelectronic ions SO_3^{2-} and ClO_3^- are obtained by co-ordination of three O^{2-} ions to S^{4+} and Cl^{5+} ions, which already have two electrons in excess of the inert-gas structure, and consequently achieve an octet of electrons in the complex oxy-anions. These anions thus form part of a tetrahedral unit, and are pyramidal in structure.

In the same way, the ion CO_3^{2-} can be derived from the inert-gas type ion C^{4+}, and its plane triangular shape arises from the sextet of electrons obtained by co-ordination of three O^{2-} ions. The ion NO_2^-, derived from N^{3+} also has a sextet of electrons, and as only two of the three pairs are bonding, the ion forms a fragment of a triangular structure and is bent, the bond angle in crystalline sodium nitrite being 115°.

Co-ordination Number

In the compounds so far discussed the number of atoms surrounding any particular atom is limited by the number of bonding electrons available, but in co-ordination compounds there is no limitation of this sort, since each additional ligand atom brings its bonding electrons with it. The question then arises of what factors are responsible for determining co-ordination numbers.

A survey of co-ordination compounds of all the elements reveals that the co-ordination number of four is not exceeded in elements of the first short period, that a co-ordination number of six is very rarely exceeded in the second short or first long period, and that co-ordination numbers greater than six are common in elements of the second, third and fourth long periods. This suggests that the most important factor determining co-ordination number is the size of the central atom, though the restriction of the co-ordination number to four in the first short period can also be explained by the non-availability of *d*-orbitals of suitable energy.

In the second short and first long periods, the maximum co-ordination number is normally six, despite the occurrence of a very few compounds with co-ordination numbers of seven or eight. However, even the co-ordination number of six is not always achieved in compounds of these elements. Lower co-ordination numbers, usually four, are observed in particular with halide ions, oxide ions or sulphide ions as ligands, though co-ordination numbers of six are usual with fluoride ions, water molecules and some other sulphur donors. Halide ions can usually be accommodated in 6:co-ordinate compounds with mixed ligands and some ligands which alone give 6:co-ordinate complexes, can be incorporated in 4:co-ordinate complexes which also have halide ions as ligands.

It has long been recognized that metal–ligand bond distances are not the same in octahedral and tetrahedral complexes; this difference was expressed by Pauling in terms of different octahedral and tetrahedral radii for the central ions. However, now that a much larger number of structure determinations has been done, it has become apparent that the difference in metal–ligand bond distances is not such a simple function of co-ordination number. Table 10 shows the average observed bond lengths in complexes of first row transition metals with six common ligands. Where the ligand is a halide ion, the bond length is greater in octahedral

TABLE 10. AVERAGE METAL–LIGAND BOND LENGTHS OBSERVED IN TETRAHEDRAL AND OCTAHEDRAL COMPLEXES (Å)

Ligand	I^-	Br^-	Cl^-	H_2O	NCS^-	NH_3
Octahedral	2·85	2·60	2·38	2·06	2·09	2·04
Tetrahedral	2·53	2·41	2·30	2·0	2·15	2·05

complexes than in tetrahedral; it was from such data that the different octahedral and tetrahedral radii were obtained; but, with oxygen or nitrogen donors, there is no difference in bond length. The data imply that in octahedral mixed complexes, halide ions are crowded out. The lower co-ordination number observed in pure halide complexes thus appears to be the result of steric overcrowding of the ligands, and could be explained in terms of ligand–ligand interaction.

When an atom is surrounded by a group of electron-pairs, the greatest electron-pair repulsion is between non-bonding pairs. In the same way, the greatest repulsion between neighbouring ligand atoms can be expected when these atoms carry the largest number of non-bonding electron pairs in the valence shell, hence with the halide ions, oxide and sulphide. Within a series of similar ligands, such as F^-, Cl^-, Br^-, I^-, simple size effects can be expected to lead to lower co-ordination numbers with the larger donor atoms. Steric considerations of this sort appear to provide the most satisfactory explanation of variations of co-ordination number in complexes of ions in the second short and first long periods.

Spectrochemical Series

So long as the point-charge crystal-field model is retained, it is not possible to account for the position of the various ligands in the spectrochemical series, but if this model is modified so as to recognize that position in the series represents the ability to *discriminate* between d_ϵ and d_γ-orbitals, and not the absolute effect of ligands on the *d*-orbital energies, it becomes possible to account for the series by an extension of the Sidgwick–Powell approach.

In an octahedral complex, one pair of electrons on the donor atom points directly at the d_γ-orbitals, but the remaining donor-atom electron-pairs are in a position to interact with the d_ϵ-orbitals; it is these which are ignored in the point-charge model. These electron-pairs will react with the d_ϵ-orbitals most considerably when they are non-bonding pairs. If the d_γ-donor pair interaction is regarded as approximately constant, the d_ϵ-interaction will increase as the number of non-bonding electron-pairs on the donor atom increases; but increasing d_ϵ-interaction means less discrimination between d_ϵ and d_γ, and so, an earlier place in the spectrochemical series. The position of a ligand in the series should thus depend primarily on the number of non-bonding electron-pairs on the donor atom. That this is so, is shown in the following shortened form of the series in which the number of non-bonding pairs on the donor atom in the free ligand is also shown:

$$\underbrace{I^-, Br^-, Cl^-, F^-}_{4}, \underbrace{OH^-, RCO_2^-}_{3}, \underbrace{H_2O, \mathit{N}CS}_{2}, \underbrace{NH_3, py, en, dipy, CN^-}_{1}$$

Within any one of the four groups d_ϵ/d_γ, discrimination increases as the donor atom electron pairs become less diffuse, hence the order of the halide ions. Cyanide ion is almost unique in having a single isolated pair of electrons, all the others being "pinned back" in the triple bond.

In this chapter a number of different theoretical approaches have been outlined. None of these approaches alone is satisfactory for the treatment of all sorts of molecules and complex ions, but one or another, or some combination of them, usually provides a deeper insight into experimentally observed properties, and co-ordination chemists make use of whichever approach appears most likely to be successful in the discussion of any particular problem.

FURTHER READING

BARNARD, A. K., *Theoretical Basis of Inorganic Chemistry*, McGraw-Hill, New York (1965).

CARTMEL, E. and FOWLES, G. W. A., *Valency and Molecular Structure*, 2nd ed., Butterworth, London (1961).

JORGENSEN, C. K., *Absorption Spectra and Chemical Bonding in Complexes*, Pergamon, Oxford (1962).

ORGEL, L. E., *An Introduction to the Chemistry of Transition Metals*, Methuen, London (1960).

PAULING, L., *The Nature of the Chemical Bond*, 3rd ed., Cornell University Press, New York (1960).

SELWOOD, P. W., *Magnetochemistry*, 2nd ed., Interscience, New York (1956).

BASCH, H., VISTE, A. and GRAY, H. B., Molecular orbital theory for octahedral and tetrahedral metal complexes, *J. Chem. Phys.* **44**, 10 (1966).

COTTON, F. A., The infrared spectra of transition metal complexes, *Modern Coordination Chemistry*, Eds. LEWIS, J. and WILKINS, R. G., Interscience, New York (1960).

CRAIG, D. P. and NYHOLM, R. S., The nature of the metal–ligand bond, *Chelating Agents and Metal Chelates*, Eds. MELLOR, D. P. and DWYER, F. P., Academic Press, New York (1964).

DUNN, T. M., The visible and ultraviolet spectra of complex compounds, *Modern Co-ordination Chemistry*, Eds. LEWIS, J. and WILKINS, R. G., Interscience, New York (1960).

FIGGIS, B. N. and LEWIS, J., The magnetochemistry of complex compounds, *Modern Coordination Chemistry*, Eds. LEWIS, J. and WILKINS, R. G., Interscience, New York (1960).

FIGGIS, B. N. and LEWIS, J., Magnetic properties of transition metal complexes, *Progress in Inorg. Chem.* **6**, 37 (1964).

GRIFFITH, J. S. and ORGEL, L. E., Ligand-field theory, *Quart. Rev.* **11**, 381 (1957).

HARTMANN, K., New tendencies in theories of complex ions, *Pure and Applied Chem.* **10**, 1 (1965).

NYHOLM, R. S., Magnetism and inorganic chemistry, *Quart. Rev.* **7**, 377 (1953).

NYHOLM, R. S. and GILLESPIE, R. J., Inorganic stereochemistry, *Quart. Rev.* **11**, 339 (1957).

NYHOLM, R. S. and MACCOLL, A., The stereochemistry of complex compounds, *Progress in Stereochemistry* **1**, 322 (1954).

ORGEL, L. E., Charge-transfer spectra and some related phenomena, *Quart. Rev.* **8**, 422 (1954).

SUTTON, L. E., The theory of bonding in metal complexes, *J. Inorg. Nucl. Chem.* **8**, 23 (1958).

CHAPTER III

TRANSITION METAL STEREOCHEMISTRY

WHILE classical methods were able to establish the stereochemistry of some transition metal ions, notably the octahedral environment of the Co^{3+}, Cr^{3+} and Pt^{4+} ions in their complex compounds and the formation of square-planar complexes by the Pt^{2+}, Pd^{2+} and Ni^{2+} ions, these methods failed when applied to some other ions, such as Cu^{2+} and Co^{2+}. The reason for this failure was the lability of the complexes of these ions, which could not be preserved intact through the processes of separation of optical or geometrical isomers. Classical methods are also restricted to deciding between such stereochemical configurations as may have been imagined, while taking no account of other possible configurations which have not been thought of. In practice, classical methods are limited to distinguishing between octahedral, tetrahedral and square-planar complexes of high stability, and this limitation has led to a widely held belief that all complex compounds must have one or other of these configurations. However, recent X-ray studies of numerous complex compounds, particularly of metals in the first transition series, have revealed a bewildering variety of stereochemical configurations, and even the distinction between the three most common configurations is often blurred.

The divalent and trivalent ions of first row transition metals are of comparable size to the ions Mg^{2+} and Al^{3+}, due to a transition metal contraction similar to that observed in the lanthanide elements. Table 1 gives Pauling's values of these ionic radii; while these values probably need revising in the light of the rapidly increasing amount of X-ray data, they show clearly the relationship of the size of these ions relative to those of neighbouring elements.

TABLE 1. RADII OF DIVALENT AND TRIVALENT IONS (Å)

	Ca	Sc	Ti	V	Cr	Mn	Fe	Co	Ni	Cu	Zn	Mg	Al
M^{2+}	0·99	—	0·90	0·88	0·84	0·80	0·76	0·74	0·72	—	0·74	0·65	0·50
M^{3+}	—	0·81	0·76	0·74	0·69	0·66	0·64	0·63	0·62	—	—	—	0·50

Data from Pauling, *Nature of the Chemical Bond*, 3rd ed., p. 518.

The ionization energies of these elements are also comparable (Table 2), so that differences of co-ordination number can rarely be attributed to the needs of the electroneutrality principle (see Chapter IV). Differences in stereochemistry between one transition metal and another must thus be discussed in terms of the effects of incompletely filled *d*-orbitals, and for this purpose a detailed account of the stereochemistry of the d^0-ions, Mg^{2+} and Al^{3+} and the d^{10}-ion, Zn^{2+}, is an essential prerequisite.

TABLE 2. IONIZATION ENERGIES (kcal/g-atom)

	Ca	Sc	Ti	V	Cr	Mn	Fe	Co	Ni	Cu	Zn	Mg	Al
1st	141	151	157	155	156	171	181	181	176	178	216	176	138
2nd	274	295	313	338	380	360	373	393	418	468	414	346	434

Data from Pauling, *Nature of the Chemical Bond*, 3rd ed., p. 57.

BERYLLIUM, MAGNESIUM AND ALUMINIUM

The classical observation that the small Be^{2+} ion forms tetrahedral complexes, has been confirmed by several X-ray studies, including the $[BeF_4]^{2-}$ ion in Li_2BeF_4 and $(NH_4)_2BeF_4$ and the hydrated ion $[Be(OH_2)_4]^{2+}$ in the sulphate. Beryllium acetylacetonate (I) has also been shown to form tetrahedral molecules; readily obtained by reaction of beryllium hydroxide with acetylacetone, this compound melts at 108°C, boils without decomposition at 270°C, and is readily soluble and monomeric in many organic solvents. In basic beryllium acetate a central 4:co-

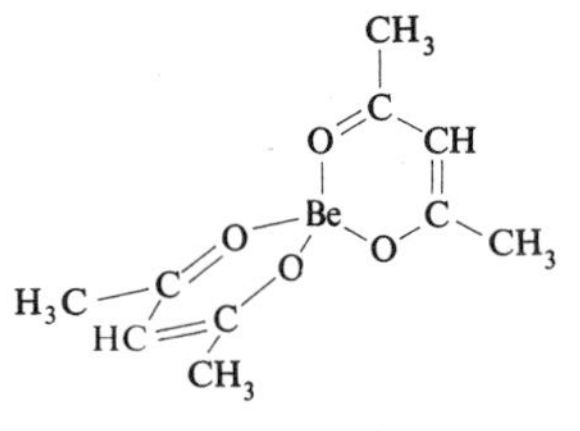

I

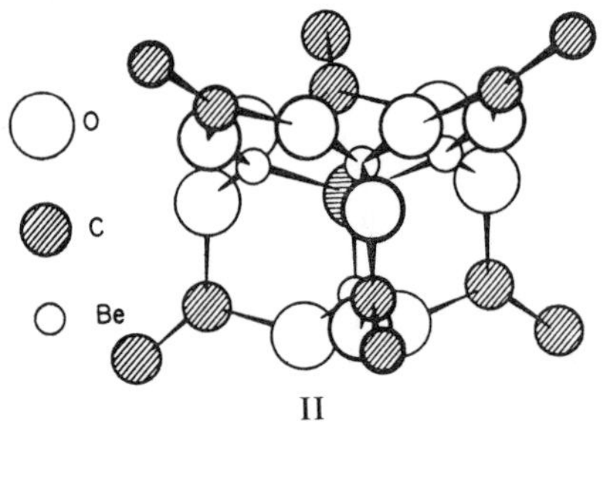

II

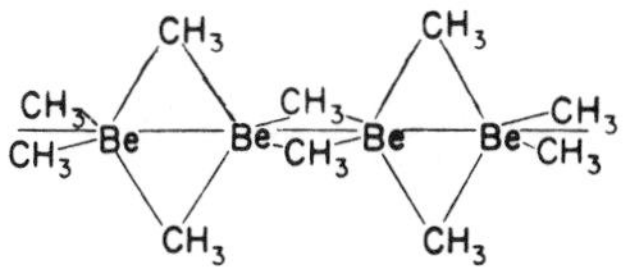

III

ordinate oxygen atom is surrounded by four tetrahedral beryllium atoms, which are linked by bridging acetate groups (II); this compound melts at 285°C, is volatile above 330°C and monomeric in the vapour and in solution in organic solvents. Tetrahedral stereochemistry is also preserved in the polymeric beryllium alkyls such as dimethyl beryllium (III).

By contrast with beryllium, the larger magnesium ion appears to be invariably 6:co-ordinate, and forms octahedral complexes. This rather remarkable distinction can be explained in terms of valence-bond theory by the unavailability of *d*-orbitals in the Be^{2+} ion, these orbitals being essential for the accommodation of six donor groups in an octahedral complex.

Few magnesium complexes have been examined by X-ray analysis, though the ion $[Mg(OH_2)_6]^{2+}$ has been shown to be octahedral in the sulphate $MgSO_4.6H_2O$ and in the benzenesulphonate; the mean Mg—O distance of 2·05 Å is comparable to that observed in many transition metal aquated complexes, and suggests that the difference of about 0·1 Å between the Pauling radii of magnesium and transition metal ions may be unreal. The magnesium ion also has an octahedral environment in the oxide, MgO, hydroxide, $Mg(OH)_2$, and in numerous silicates and basic salts, of which the simplest is the mineral olivine, Mg_2SiO_4, in which the Mg^{2+} ion is surrounded octahedrally by six oxygen atoms from discrete tetrahedral SiO_4^{4-} ions. The co-ordination chemistry of magnesium is restricted by the instability of its complexes with ligands in which the donor atoms are not oxygen (see Chapter V), but it is clearly 6:co-ordinate in inner complexes such as the acetylacetone and 8:hydroxyquinoline derivatives, which crystallize as dihydrates. The acetylacetonate is readily dehydrated by heating to about 100°C, but the anhydrous compound, which might be expected to contain 4:co-ordinate magnesium, is probably polymeric and 6:co-ordinate, as it is quite insoluble in organic solvents.

Aluminium forms both octahedral and tetrahedral complexes. The tetrahedral environment of the aluminium atom is observed in the complex halide $Na[AlCl_4]$ and in dimeric molecules of the aluminium halides, in which one of the non-bonding electron-pairs on one AlX_3 unit is donated to the aluminium atom of the other (IV).

The Al—X bonds within the bridge are equal but longer than the ter-

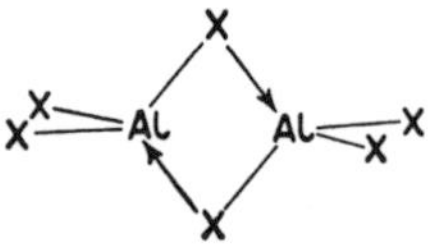

IV

minal Al – X bonds; this difference in bond lengths decreases with increasing size of the halogen atom; actual bond distances are shown in Table 3.

TABLE 3. BOND DISTANCES IN DIMERIC ALUMINIUM HALIDES (Å)

Halogen	Length of Al—X bond	
	bridge	terminal
Chloride	2·21	2·06
Bromide	2·33	2·21
Iodide	2·58	2·53

On heating, the dimers dissociate reversibly at 400–600°C, the monomeric molecules being plane triangular. The bromide and iodide retain the dimeric structure in the solid state, but solid aluminium chloride has a layer lattice in which the aluminium is 6:co-ordinate.

The dialkyl aluminium halides, R_2AlX, and the corresponding alkoxides, R_2AlOR', are also dimeric in solution and in the vapour state, and the trialkoxides are polymeric, $[Al(OR)_3]_n$. One of the most striking examples of tetrahedral co-ordination of aluminium occurs in the aluminium alkyls, AlR_3, which form dimeric molecules (V) despite the electron-deficient nature of the dimers produced.

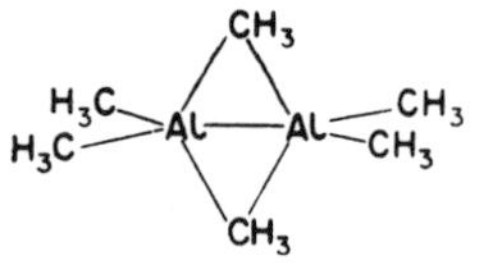

V

The nature of the bonding in these compounds is now explained in terms of "three-centred bonds" produced by overlap of sp^3-hybrid-bond-orbitals on the bridging carbon atoms with sp^3-orbitals on each aluminium atom (VI); the polymeric beryllium alkyls can be accounted for on the same basis.

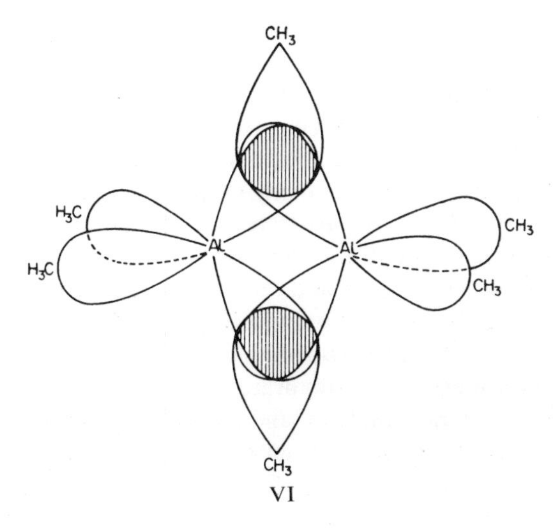

VI

With fluorine or oxygen as donor atoms, however, aluminium is usually 6:co-ordinate, and the octahedral environment has been confirmed by X-ray analysis of the mineral cryolite, $Na_3[AlF_6]$, and many other complex fluorides, the hydroxide and numerous silicates. Inner complexes of aluminium such as the acetylacetonate and 8:hydroxyquinoline derivative are soluble and monomeric in organic solvents; trichelate anions, such as the complex oxalate, $[Al(C_2O_4)_3]^{3-}$, have been resolved into optical isomers.

ZINC

The stereochemistry of zinc has been extensively studied. Many of its compounds are isomorphous with those of magnesium, the zinc atoms being octahedrally co-ordinated: the $[Zn(OH_2)_6]^{2+}$ ion has been shown to be octahedral by X-ray analysis of $Zn(ClO_4)_2.6H_2O$, $Zn(BrO_3)_2.6H_2O$, $ZnSO_4.7H_2O$ and the benzenesulphonate hexahydrate; the mean Zn—O distance in these compounds is 2·12 Å, compared with about 2·05 Å in $[Mg(OH_2)_6]^{2+}$. The zinc ion is also surrounded by six

VII VIII

oxygen atoms (mean 2·15 Å) in $ZnCO_3$ and $ZnWO_4$. The crystal structure of zinc acetate is unusual in containing *cis*-octahedral molecules of dihydrate, in which the acetate ions act as bidentate ligands forming four-membered rings (VII); the zinc–oxygen distances are comparable to those in the hexaquo-ion, the four carboxyl oxygen atoms being at a distance of 2·18 Å and two water oxygens at 2·14. The 8:hydroxyquinoline compound crystallizes as dihydrate, like the magnesium compound; X-ray analysis shows that it has the *trans*-octahedral structure (VIII), but the bonds between the zinc and the chelate are rather short (2·05 Å) and the water molecules are held only weakly (Zn—O 2·27 Å).

Zinc histidinate has also been shown to contain zinc atoms in a distorted octahedral environment; the dihydrate and pentahydrate have both been examined by X-ray analysis and contain similar zinc histidinate molecules in which four nitrogen atoms form a flattened tetrahedron round the zinc atom (Zn—N 2·00–2·05 Å) with the oxygen atoms of two carboxyl groups completing a very distorted octahedron at much greater distances (2·91 Å) (IX).

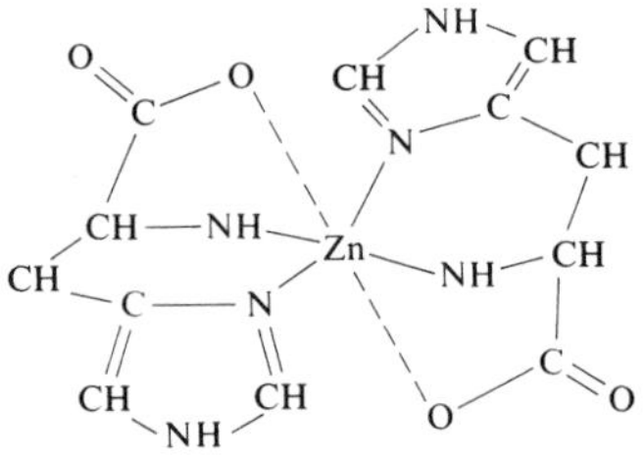

IX

In many other compounds, particularly those with large or highly charged anions, zinc resembles beryllium, and has co-ordination number four; these include the sulphide, ZnS, and oxide, ZnO, and the silicate Zn_2SiO_4, which are isostructural with the corresponding beryllium compounds but different from the magnesium compounds. Zinc also resembles beryllium in forming a basic acetate, $Zn_4O(CH_3CO_2)_6$, with a similar structure; in this and in zinc oxide the Zn—O distances are shorter than in the 6:co-ordinate compounds, and average 1·96 Å. Zinc has also been shown to have a tetrahedral environment in the neutral complexes $ZnCl_2(NH_3)_2$ and $ZnBr_2(NH_3)_2$ and in the complex anions $[ZnCl_4]^{2-}$ and $[ZnBr_4]^{2-}$. It is interesting to note that the corresponding cadmium compounds, $CdCl_2.2NH_3$ and $CdBr_2.2NH_3$ are 6:co-ordinate, and form polymeric chains with halogen bridges (X); furthermore, when cadmium chloride reacts with potassium chloride, the complex chloride formed has the formula K_4CdCl_6, and has been shown to contain octahedral $[CdCl_6]^{4-}$ ions. Cadmium is not, however, exclusively 6:co-ordinate, and the tetrahedral ion $[Cd(NH_3)_4]^{2+}$ has been shown to occur in the perrhenate.

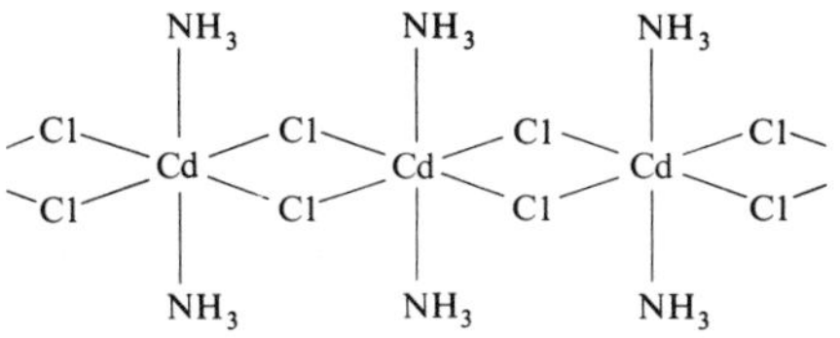

X

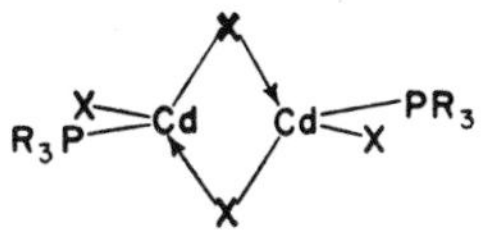

XI

Cadmium and mercury also form a number of compounds, in which tetrahedral co-ordination of the metal atom is maintained by dimerization, such as the trialkylphosphine complexes of cadmium and mercuric halides (XI). Tetrahedral co-ordination is also preserved in zinc and cadmium cyanides, the cyanide ions acting as double donors, forming linear M—C≡N—M links throughout the crystal.

In some zinc compounds, both octahedral and tetrahedral stereochemistries occur together: in the basic chloride, $Zn_5(OH)_8Cl_2.H_2O$, for example, three-fifths of the zinc atoms are surrounded by six oxygen atoms at the corners of an octahedron (Zn—O 2·16 Å) and two-fifths are tetrahedrally co-ordinated by four oxygen atoms (Zn—O 2·02 Å) and in the basic sulphate $Zn_2(OH)_2SO_4$, half of the zinc atoms have an octahedral environment in which the sulphate ions take part as bidentate ligands (Zn—O 1·95–2·20 Å) and half have a tetrahedral environment (Zn—O 1·94–2·06 Å).

The difference between the zinc–oxygen bond lengths in octahedral compounds (about 2·12 Å) and in tetrahedral (about 1·98 Å) has been interpreted in terms of differing bond types, the longer bonds being regarded as ionic and the shorter as covalent, but the recent discovery of 5:co-ordinate zinc compounds raises doubts about the interpretation of these bond distances in these terms. The first established 5:co-ordinate compound was terpyridyl zinc chloride (XII), in which the configuration about the zinc atom is trigonal-bipyramidal, somewhat distorted by the demands of the organic tridentate ligand; the 5:co-ordinate structure observed is particularly surprising in view of the ready availability of an alternative 4:co-ordinated ionic structure, $[terpyZnCl]^+Cl^-$, or 6:co-ordinated structures with bridging halogen atoms. The cadmium compound is similar and is the only known example of 5:co-ordinate cadmium.

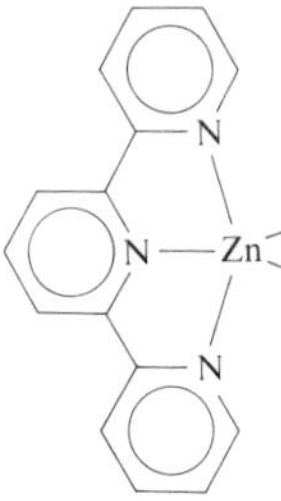

XII 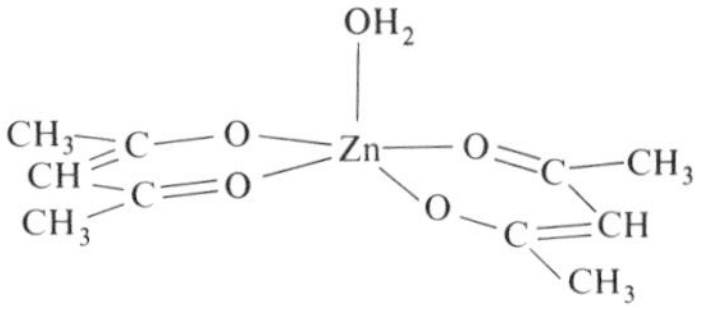 XIII

Zinc acetylacetonate is also remarkable in crystallizing from aqueous solution as monohydrate; the crystals have been shown to contain 5:co-ordinate molecules, the shape of which is in between trigonal-bipyramidal and square-pyramidal, but nearer to the latter, with five equal Zn—O distances of 2·02 Å (XIII). The dihydrate, which would be expected to be isostructural with the cobalt compound, cannot be made, but the anhydrous compound is readily obtained by heating the hydrate, and is probably trimeric like the nickel compound (p. 74), in the solid state, though soluble and monomeric in hydrocarbon solvents, so presumably tetrahedral in solution. By reaction with heterocyclic bases, compounds of the types $Zn(acac)_2base$ and $Zn(acac)_2base_2$, are obtained; these are soluble in benzene and other organic solvents, the compounds $Zn(acac)_2base$ dissolving without dissociation, whereas those with two molecules of base dissociate with the loss of one of these molecules of base; apparently, therefore, the co-ordination number five is preferred in solutions of these compounds; similar behaviour has been observed with the corresponding benzoylacetone and dibenzoylmethane derivatives.

Five co-ordination of zinc has also been observed in crystalline disalicylidene-ethylenediiminato-zinc monohydrate (XIV), which can be obtained by adding aqueous zinc acetate solution to a solution of disalicylidene-ethylenediamine in acetone; in this compound the zinc atom lies at the centre of gravity of a square pyramid of ligand atoms of which the water oxygen forms the apex. The water molecule can be replaced by heterocyclic bases, and by carrying out the preparation of the compound in alcoholic solution it is obtained anhydrous; the structure of the anhydrous compound is not known, but anhydrous bis(N-methyl-salicylaldiminato)zinc also contains 5:co-ordinate zinc atoms and is dimeric (XV).

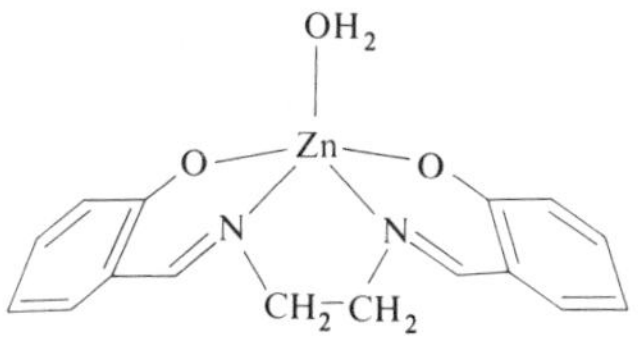

XIV

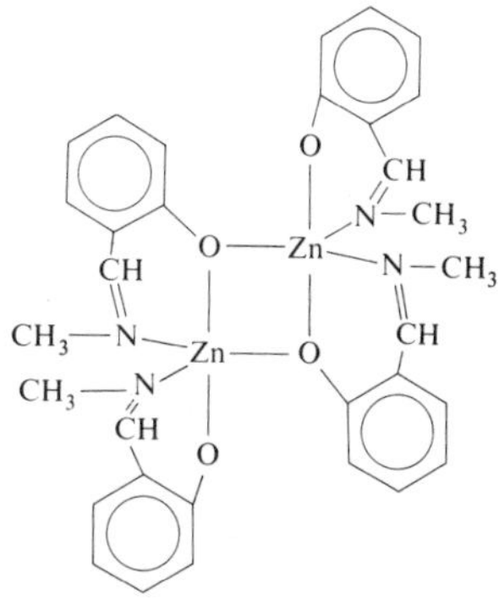

XV

COPPER

The singly charged d^{10}-ion Cu^+, differs markedly from the isoelectronic Zn^{2+} ion: its more stable complexes are formed by ligands with carbon, sulphur, phosphorus or halogens as donor atoms (see Chapter V), and its co-ordination number is usually lower. Many copper(I) complexes are 4:co-ordinate and tetrahedral, for example, the complex cyanide ion $[Cu(CN)_4]^{3-}$ and the tetrathioacetamide cation in $[Cu(CH_3CS.NH_2)_4]^+Cl^-$.

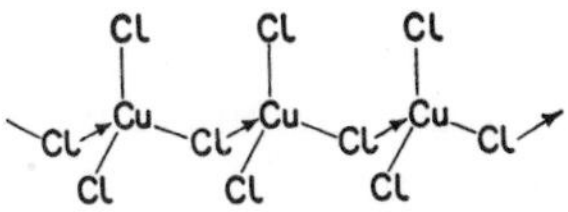

XVI

The cuprous halides and silver iodide also have structures in which the metal ions are surrounded tetrahedrally by halide ions (zinc blende structures), despite the comparatively large size of the metal ions (the cuprous ion has almost exactly the same radius as the sodium ion and the silver ion is, of course, larger), which would readily allow the ionic rock salt structure, which is in fact adopted by silver bromide and chloride. It appears therefore that we should regard these cuprous halides and silver iodide as three-dimensional co-ordination systems. This idea is supported by the crystal structure of the double alkali metal cuprous chlorides, M_2CuCl_3, in which the $CuCl_3^{2-}$ anions form chain polymers, the cuprous ion being tetrahedrally surrounded by chloride ions (XVI). The tetrahedral environment of the copper atoms is also preserved in chalcopyrite (copper pyrites), $CuFeS_2$, which has a wurtzite structure with alternate copper and iron atoms, clear evidence that the substance is cuprous ferric sulphide and not cupric ferrous.

One of the most remarkable examples of the preservation of a tetrahedral environment for cuprous and argentous ions occurs in the triethylarsine complexes of the metal iodides, $MI.As(C_2H_5)_3$, which are tetrameric, with the copper or silver and iodine atoms forming a "box" of distorted cubic shape (XVII). The curious tetrameric thallous alkoxides probably have somewhat similar structures (XVIII). One interesting feature of

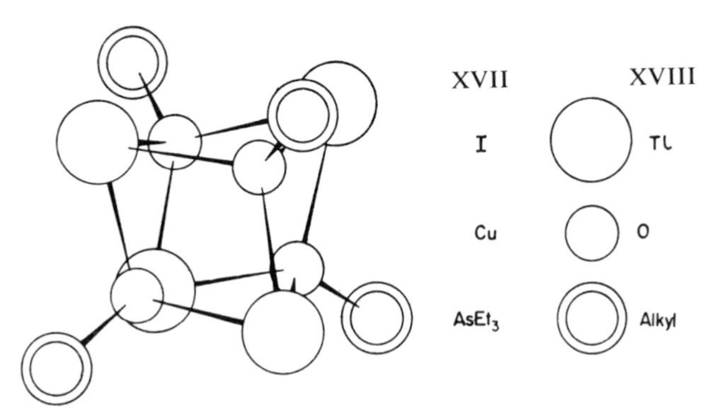

Box like molecule of $[CuI.As(C_2H_5)_3]_4$ (XVII) or $[Tl\ OAlk]_4$ (XVIII)

these box-like tetrameric structures is that the tetrahedral co-ordination of the Cu^+, Ag^+ or oxygen atoms imposes bond angles considerably less than 90° at the iodine or thallium atoms, suggesting that these atoms may be forming hybrid-bond orbitals without the participation of the *s*-orbitals – an unusual example of the "inert pair" effect.

The larger d^{10}-ions of silver, gold and mercury generally prefer a co-ordination number of two, the 2:co-ordinated groups forming a linear arrangement with the central metal atom as in the silver ammine, $[Ag(NH_3)_2]^+$ and aurocyanide, $[Au(CN)_2]^-$ ions and molecules of the mercuric halides or mercury–organic compounds. This preference is shown in the structures of silver and cuprous oxides, each oxide ion being tetrahedrally co-ordinated to four metal ions and each metal ion linearly to two oxide ions, so that the overall pattern is of oxygen atoms arranged tetrahedrally about one another with cuprous or silver ions in the middle of the O—M—O links in rather the same way as the CN^- ions are placed in zinc cyanide. When the linearly co-ordinated metal ions are combined with doubly co-ordinating anions, the result is the formation of a chain structure; in silver cyanide the chains are straight due to the linear disposition of the co-ordinating bonds of the cyanide ions (XIXa) but

→Ag—C≡N→Ag—C≡N→Ag—C≡N→Ag—C≡N→ XIXa

→Ag—S—C≡N→Ag—S—C≡N→Ag—S—C≡N→ XIXb

in the thiocyanate a zig-zag chain is produced due to the bond angle at the sulphur atoms (XIXb). Zig-zag chains also occur in aurous iodide, and in mercuric oxide the dihedral angle at the oxygen atoms leads to a spiral arrangement of the chains.

Replacement of the symmetrical d^{10}-group of electrons by a d^9-group can be expected to have the effect of lowering the symmetry of the complexes formed; in octahedral complexes the single unpaired electron could be placed in either the d_z^2 or the $d_{x-y}^{2\ \ 2}$ orbital:

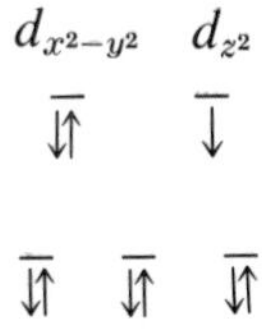

$d_{x^2-y^2}$ d_{z^2} $d_{x^2-y^2}$ d_{z^2}

⇃↾ ↓ ↓ ⇃↾

XX XXI

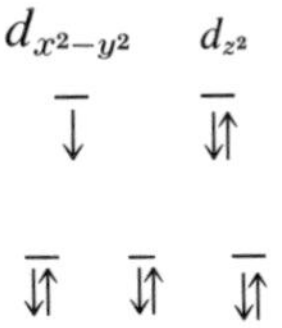

⇃↾ ⇃↾ ⇃↾ ⇃↾ ⇃↾ ⇃↾

and in either case would produce unequal ligand repulsions along the different axes. In the former case (XX), larger repulsions along the *x*- and *y*-axes than along the *z*-axis should lead to a flattening of an octahedral complex, and in the latter case (XXI), the larger repulsions along the *z*-axis should lead to an elongated octahedral environment, an extreme case of which would occur in a square-planar complex. In the same way, distortions could be expected in tetrahedral complexes, and stereochemistries might be expected which are not found at all with more symmetrical cations.

In many of its simple compounds, Cu^{2+} is found in distorted octahedral co-ordination. While distortion of the octahedron by flattening is rare, it is observed in K_2CuF_4 and $KCuF_3$, in both of which Cu^{2+} ions are surrounded by six fluoride ions in three-dimensional networks, two of the fluorine atoms being closer to the copper (1·95 Å) than the other four (2·08 Å). Flattened octahedra also occur in the β form of $CuBr_2.2NH_3$, which has a halogen-bridged chain structure similar to $CdCl_2.NH_3$ (X). (Cu—4Br 2·88 Å, Cu—2N 2·03 Å).

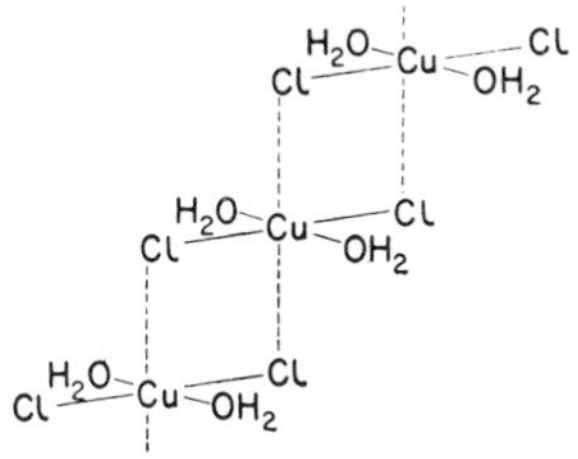

H2O Cu Cl
Cl OH2
H2O Cu Cl
Cl OH2
H2O Cu Cl
Cl OH2

XXII

In the α form of $CuBr_2 2NH_3$ and in $CuCl_2.2OH_2$, there are square-planar molecules so arranged that the chlorine (or bromine) atoms of one molecule fall just above or below the copper atoms of another (XXII), each copper atom having an environment of two O or N atoms and two halide ions in a plane with two more distant halide ions above and below, completing elongated octahedral co-ordination; a similar structure is adopted in $CuCl_2.2py$ (py = pyridine) and in the double salts $CuCl_2.2KCl.2OH_2$ and $CuBr_2.2NH_4Br.2OH_2$. The distances from the copper atoms to its neighbours in some of these compounds are shown in Table 4.

TABLE 4. DISTANCES FROM COPPER ATOM TO NEAREST NEIGHBOURS IN ELONGATED OCTAHEDRAL COMPLEXES OF Cu^{2+}

Compound	Distance to nearest neighbours (Å)		
CuF_2	4F 1·93		2F 2·27
$CuF_2.2OH_2$	2F 1·89	2O 1·93	2F 2·47
$CuCl_2$	4Cl 2·30		2Cl 2·95
$CuCl_2.2OH_2$	2Cl 2·28	2O 1·93	2Cl 2·95
$CuCl_2.2KCl.2OH_2$	2Cl 2·32	2O 1·97	2Cl 2·95
$CuCl_2.2py$	2Cl 2·28	2N 2·02	2Cl 3·05
$CuCl_2$.triazole	2Cl 2·34	2N 1·98	2Cl 2·77
$CuBr_2$	4Br 2·40		2Br 3·18
$CuBr_2.2NH_3(\alpha)$	2Br 2·54	2N 1·93	2Br 3·08
Cu.prolinate	2N 1·99	2O 2·03	2O 2·52

In anhydrous copper(II) chloride (and bromide) the copper and chlorine atoms are arranged in chains so that each copper atom is at the centre of a square of chlorine atoms (XXIII). A similar arrangement is adopted in the divalent halides of palladium and platinum (see p. 19), but there is a significant difference between the $CuCl_2$ structure and that of these halides: in $CuCl_2$ the chains are so packed that the chlorine atoms forming part of one chain, also complete elongate octahedral co-ordination of the copper atoms in neighbouring chains (XXIV), (XXV), whereas in the $PdCl_2$ structure the chains are packed as if they were organic molecules, and the palladium atoms have true square-planar co-ordination (XXVI).

A similar environment of the copper atoms is found in the complex halides $KCuCl_3$ and $KCuBr_3$, but the more highly chlorinated complexes, Cs_2CuCl_4 and $[Cr(NH_3)_6]CuCl_5$, have quite different structures in which there are discrete $[CuCl_4]^{2-}$ and $[CuCl_5]^{3-}$ anions. The first of these has a tetrahedral structure in which the tetrahedron is slightly distorted (flattened), the bond angles between the Cu—Cl bonds being 118° and 104° instead of the tetrahedral angle of 109·5°; all four Cu—Cl bonds are equal in length (2·22 Å). The $[CuCl_5]^{3-}$ ion is trigonal-bipyramidal with all of the Cu—Cl bonds equal in length.

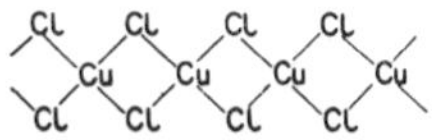

XXIII $(CuCl_2)_n$ chain

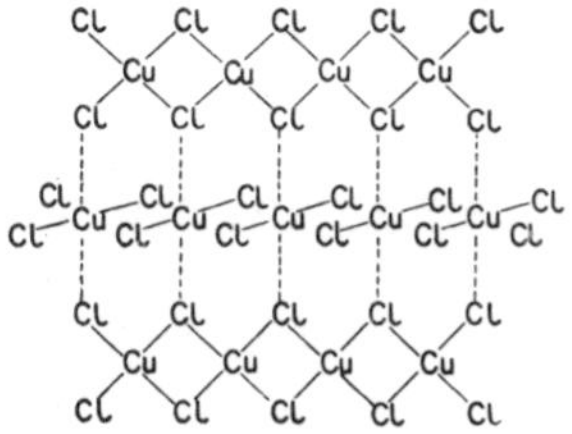

XXIV

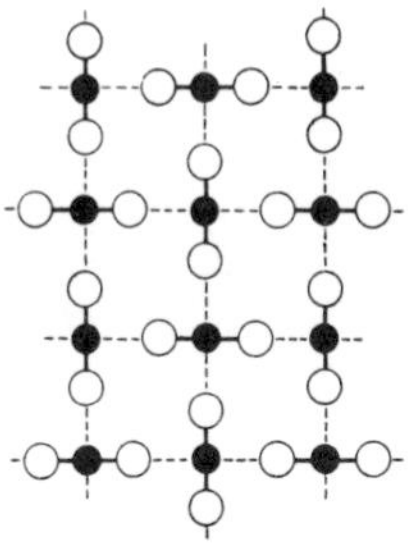

XXV

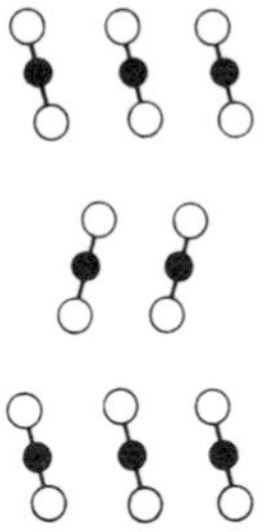

XXVI

Copper(II) sulphate, the only transition metal sulphate not belonging to the series of isomorphous heptahydrates, crystallizes at ordinary temperatures as the pentahydrate, $CuSO_4.5H_2O$. In the crystal each copper atom is surrounded by four water molecules at the corners of a square and two, more distant, oxygen atoms belonging to the sulphate ions, which complete an elongated octahedron (XXVII); the fifth water molecule is not co-ordinated to the metal atom, but links the sulphate anions and co-ordinated water molecules by hydrogen bonds.

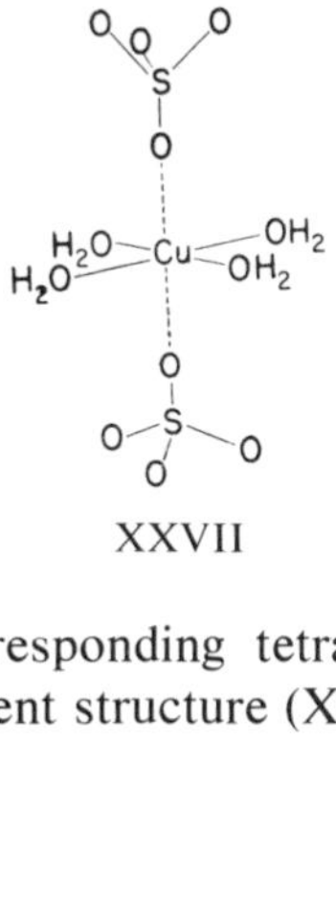

XXVII

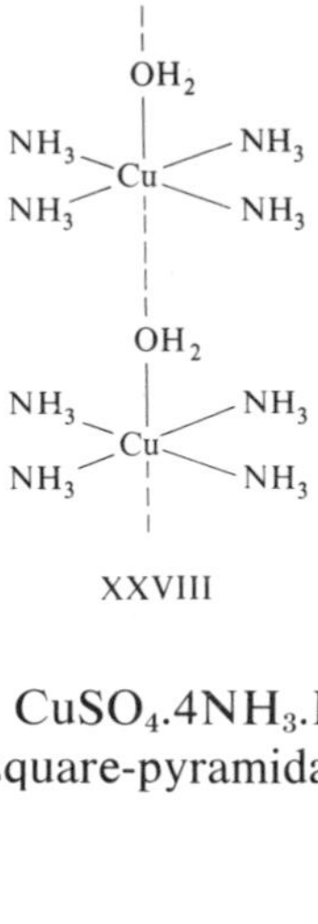

XXVIII

The corresponding tetrammine sulphate, $CuSO_4.4NH_3.H_2O$, has a quite different structure (XXVIII) in which square-pyramidal molecules are stacked up so as to give the copper atoms a co-ordination number of six; all four ammonia molecules are equivalent (Cu—N 2·05 Å), but the water molecule is much closer to one copper atom than to the next (Cu—O 2·59, 3·57 Å) and the longer distance should probably be regarded as non-bonding, so that this compound could be described as consisting of discrete square-pyramidal molecules, thus suggesting that replacement of $4Cl^-$ or $4OH_2$ by $4NH_3$ has the effect of lowering the co-ordination number.

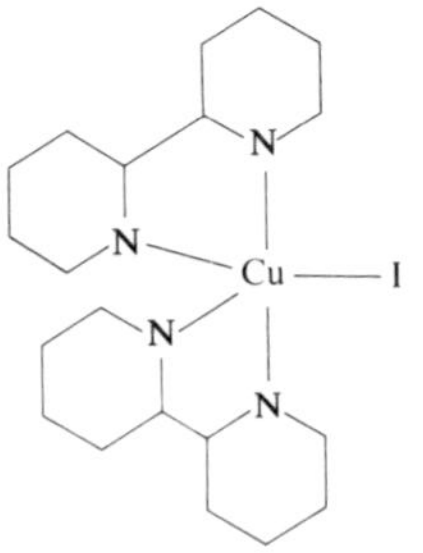

XXIX 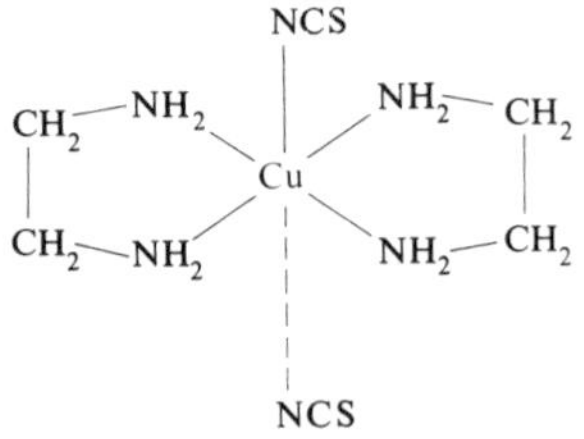 XXX

Five co-ordination of copper(II) is also observed in some other compounds in which there are four N-donors: bisdipyridyl copper(II) iodide has been shown to crystallize with the ionic structure $[Cu(dipy)_2I]^+I^-$, in which the cation is trigonal-bipyramidal (XXIX); this structure is apparently preserved in solution as this and some related compounds are uni-univalent electrolytes, as are the corresponding derivatives of 2-picolylamine; another example of this type is terpyridyl copper(II) chloride, which is isostructural with the zinc and cadmium compounds (XII). In bis(ethylenediamine)copper(II) tetrathiocyanatomercurate, square-planar $[Cu(en)_2]^{+2}$ ions are further co-ordinated by the N atoms of thiocyanate groups (Cu—N 2·7, 3·8 Å) in rather similar fashion to the co-ordination of the water molecules in the tetrammine sulphate, and this should probably be regarded as an example of square-pyramidal co-ordination (XXX); however, in bis(ethylenediamine)copper(II) thiocyanate, the planar $[Cu(en)_2]^{2+}$, have as nearest neighbours in the fifth and sixth co-ordination sites only S atoms of the SCN^- ions at the long distance of 3·27 Å, and this should, therefore, be regarded as an example of square-planar stereochemistry.

Truly square-planar co-ordination is observed in the phthalocyanine (see p. 152) and in the inner complexes with β-diketones. In the complexes formed by tropolone, acetoacetic ester, dibenzoylmethane and salicylaldehyde, there appears to be no interaction between molecules, but in the acetylacetonate, the molecules are stacked so that there is weak interaction between the copper atoms and the middle carbon atoms of neighbouring molecules (XXXI), which approach the copper atoms at a distance of 2·85 Å, and in the *N*-methylsalicylaldimine derivative the molecules are stacked so that the copper atoms form long chains throughout the crystal (XXXII), the distance between copper atoms being 3·33 Å.

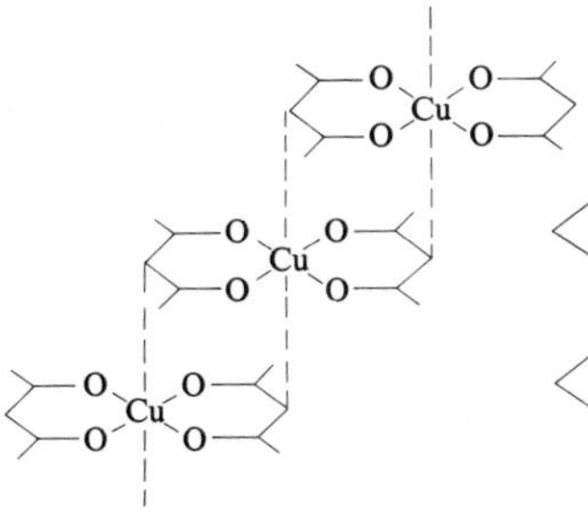

XXXI

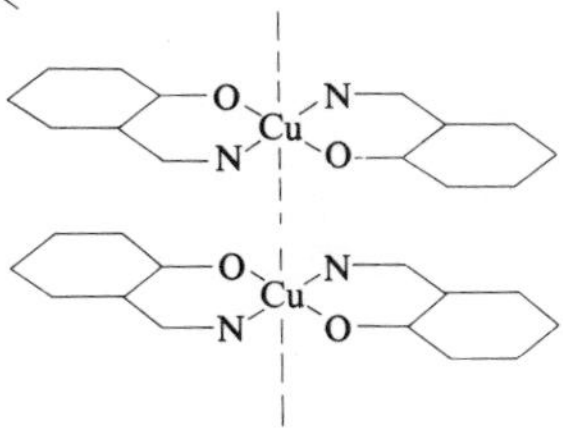

XXXII

In several other copper(II) complexes with imino-nitrogen donor atoms, square-planar molecules are slightly distorted and linked together in pairs by further co-ordination of the O-donor atoms to the copper atom of the twin molecule, which thus becomes 5:co-ordinate; examples of this are disalicylidene-ethylene-diiminato-copper(II), bis(8:hydroxy-quinolinato)copper(II) (XXXIII) and bis(dimethylglyoximato)copper(II), all of which are dimeric with oxygen bridges.

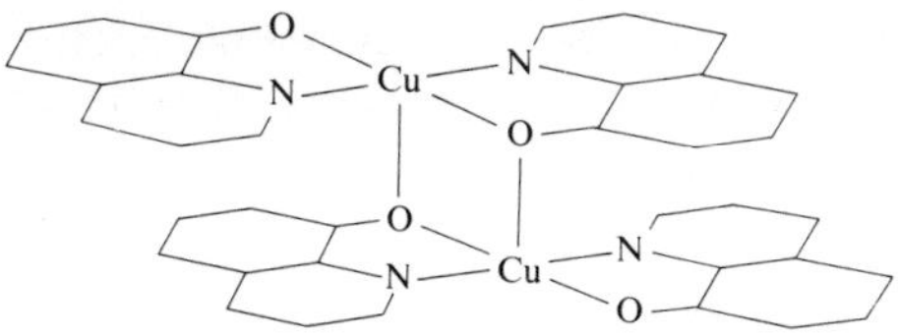

XXXIII

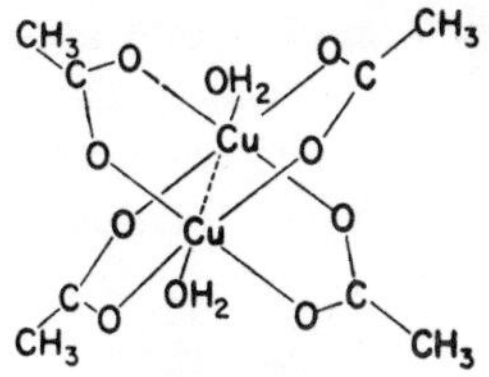

XXXIV

Another type of bridged dimer occurs in copper(II) acetate, which crystallizes as a hydrate $Cu_2(CH_3CO_2)_4(OH_2)_2$, forming box-like molecules in which the acetate ions bridge two copper atoms, each of which thus has an environment of four carboxyl oxygen atoms at the corners of a square (Cu—O 1·97 Å) and one water molecule on the axis normal to the square (Cu—O 2·20 Å); the copper atoms are actually just above the plane of the square and are separated from one another by a distance of 2·64 Å, which is about the same as that in metallic copper (XXXIV); the same molecular structure is adopted by the pyridine derivative,

$Cu_2(CH_3CO_2)_4py_2$. All these bridged compounds have abnormal magnetic properties, the effective magnetic moment of the copper atoms being reduced by antiferromagnetic interaction, though the mechanism by which this occurs is not understood. Magnetic and spectroscopic evidence indicates that the structure is preserved in solutions of copper acetate in organic solvents and in the higher homologues, and that the water molecules can be readily replaced by other ligands such as heterocyclic bases, carboxylic acids or dioxane.

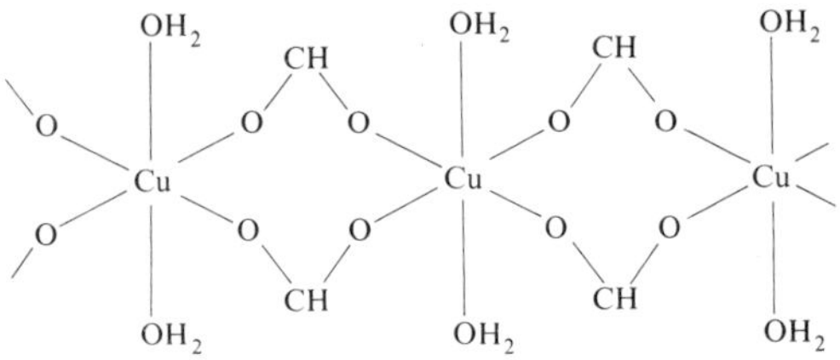

XXXV

Although this curious dimeric structure is adopted by copper(II) acetate and its higher homologues, the formate crystallizes as a tetrahydrate, which is magnetically normal and has a polymeric chain structure (XXXV) analogous to that of β-$CuBr_2(NH_3)_2$, with additional water molecules held in the lattice by hydrogen bonds; several forms of the anhydrous formate are known, all with abnormal moments.

While no evidence has been obtained for abnormal magnetic properties in the copper salts of amino acids, these present a variety of structural types. The only one known to occur as isolated hydrated molecules with elongated octahedral stereochemistry is the prolinate (XXXVI), the interatomic distances for which are quoted in Table 4.

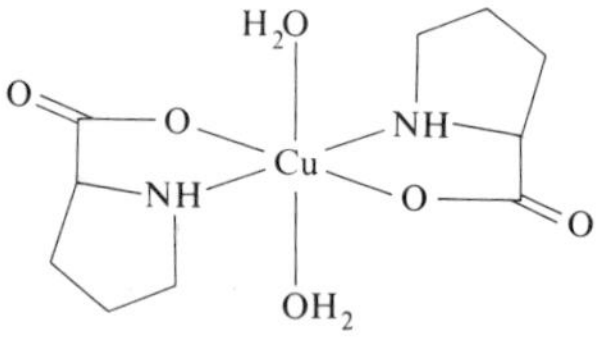

XXXVI

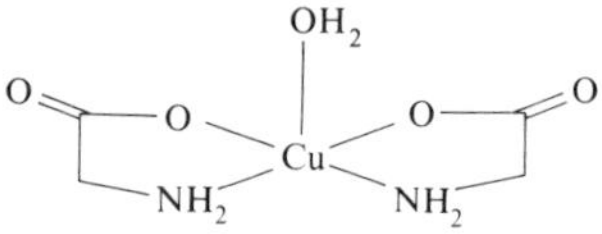

XXXVII

The glycinate crystallizes as monohydrate and is remarkable as the only known example of a copper(II) compound with a *cis*-configuration (XXXVII); two amino nitrogen and two carboxyl oxygen atoms form a square round the copper atom, the water molecule occupies the fifth site, and the carboxyl oxygen atom of a neighbouring molecule, the sixth. Higher homologues mostly crystallize anhydrous from solutions in water, elongate octahedral stereochemistry being achieved by co-ordination of the carboxyl oxygen atoms of two neighbouring molecules, though in the case of copper(II) cyclopentane-1:amino-carboxylate, the crystal is built up from isolated square-planar molecules.

The stereochemistry of copper(II) is thus very varied. The most commonly observed arrangements of ligand atoms are square planar and elongate octahedral, but 5:co-ordination is not uncommon, and there appears to be no pattern by which it would be possible to predict the stereochemistry to be adopted in any particular case, except that (as predicted by theory) regular octahedral and tetrahedral structures are not observed.

The intrinsic asymmetry of the d^9-ion, which leads to such varied stereochemistry for copper(II), is repeated in ions with a d^4-structure. Here too, high-spin octahedral complexes have an odd number of electrons in the d_γ-orbitals, and some similarity could be expected between the stereochemistry of the Cu^{2+} ion and that of Mn^{3+} and Cr^{2+}. Thus, distortions from perfect octahedral symmetry have been observed in the crystal structures of manganese(III) fluoride and tris(acetyl-acetonato)manganese(III); and chromium(II) fluoride, bromide and iodide all have structures similar to copper(II) chloride, in which the Cr^{2+} ion is surrounded by four halogen atoms at the corners of a square, and two more distant completing an elongated octahedron. The box-like dimeric structure of copper(II) acetate monohydrate (XXXIV) is repeated in the red compound $Cr_2(CH_3CO_2)_4(OH_2)_2$; but whereas anti-ferromagnetic interaction in the copper compound reduces the magnetic moment from 1·7 to 1·4β, in the chromium compound, which would be expected to have four unpaired electrons, the interaction is much stronger and this compound is diamagnetic.

We might also expect some similarity between the stereochemistry of d^9- and d^1-ions, though with the odd electron in the lower energy d-orbitals distortions are likely to be smaller, as they are in the compounds of cobalt(II). There is apparently no evidence for distortion in crystalline titanium(III) fluoride or chloride or from electron diffraction data in gaseous vanadium(IV) chloride. Most compounds of vanadium(IV), however, are oxy-compounds, such as the sulphate $VOSO_4.5H_2O$ and the acetylacetonate $VO(C_5H_7O_2)_2$. The structure of this compound has been determined: the vanadium atom lies just above the centre of the base of a square pyramid, the four bottom corners of which are occupied by oxygen atoms of the acetylacetonate rings and the apex by the odd oxygen atom (XXXVIII). The V—O distances from the metal atom to the acetylacetonate oxygen atoms are normal (1·97 Å) but the apical V—O distance is very short (1·56 Å), suggesting considerable double bonding. The compound is soluble in benzene, and its absorption spectrum in this solution is very similar to that of bis(acetylacetonato)copper(II); it also resembles the copper compound in forming addition compounds with one molecule of a base such as pyridine; the structures of these addition compounds are not known, but they are soluble in benzene and, presumably, approximately *trans*-octahedral. A basic acetylacetonate of the Ti^{4+} ion, $TiO(C_5H_7O_2)_2$, is also known, and it would be interesting to compare its structure with that of the vanadium compound.

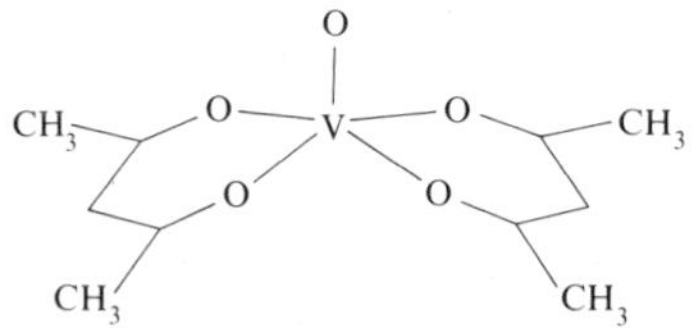

XXXVIII

NICKEL

The structural chemistry of the d^8-ions, Ni^{2+}, Pd^{2+}, Pt^{2+} and Au^{3+} is complicated by the possibility of alternative spin multiplicities. In octahedral and tetrahedral environments, only the high-spin configuration is expected since there is no possible gain in orbital energy to compensate for the energy required to enforce spin pairing (compare Figs. XXXIX and XL). High-spin octahedral complexes with the three lower *d*-orbitals completely filled and one electron in each of the upper *d*-orbitals (XL) could thus be expected to have perfect octahedral symmetry when all six ligands were alike; the tetrahedral complexes, however, could be expected to show distortions because of the unsymmetrical occupation of the upper set of *d*-orbitals by four electrons (XLI).

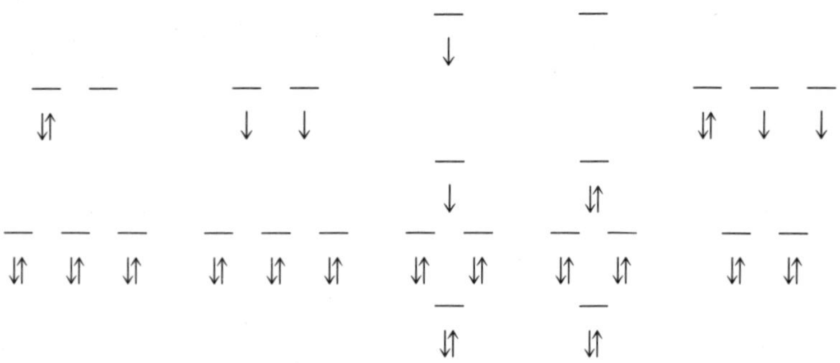

XXXIX XL XLII XLIII XLI

In square planar complexes, the choice of spin multiplicities has to be made. If the spin-pairing energy (about 43 kcal/g-atom for Ni^{2+}) exceeds the orbital separation energy between the two orbitals of highest energy in the complex, the high-spin configuration (XLII) can be expected, but if the energy separating these orbitals is greater than the energy required to enforce pairing of the electrons, then the low-spin configuration (XLIII) can be expected, in which all eight electrons are accommodated in the four lowest orbitals; in this case, since the orbitals of lowest energy are those furthest from the ligands, these filled orbitals will produce regions of high electron density above and below the molecular plane, thus stabilizing the square-planar complex against the possible attachment of one or two additional ligands.

All the known square-planar complexes formed by the second and third long period ions Pd^{2+}, Pt^{2+} and Au^{3+}, have the low-spin configuration; but in the case of Ni^{2+}, which has the lower orbital separation energy characteristic of first row transition metals, there is some evidence that high-spin configuration may be possible under some circumstances, though the usual alternative to the low-spin configuration in this case is the formation of high-spin octahedral or tetrahedral complexes.

Octahedral co-ordination of the high-spin Ni^{2+} ion is observed in numerous complexes. As expected by the theoretical approach, those complex ions in which all of the ligands are alike, such as the hydrated ion, $[Ni(OH_2)_6]^{2+}$ and the ammine and nitrite complexes, $[Ni(NH_3)_6]^{2+}$ and $[Ni(NO_2)_6]^{4-}$, are perfectly symmetrical. Other complexes with mixed ligands are all of the *trans* type. Thus, the acetate differs markedly from those of both copper(II) and zinc in crystallizing as the *trans*-tetrahydrate (XLIV), in which the acetate ion is monodentate, and the amino-acid complexes formed by glycine and β-alanine crystallize as discrete, *trans*-octahedral molecules of dihydrate (XLV).

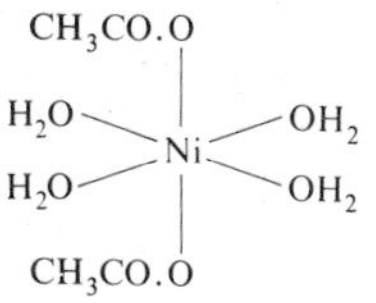

$CH_3CO.O$ / H_2O, H_2O — Ni — OH_2, OH_2 / $CH_3CO.O$

XLIV

OH_2 / CH_2–HN_2, CH_2, C(=O)–O — Ni — O–C(=O), CH_2, HN_2–CH_2 / OH_2

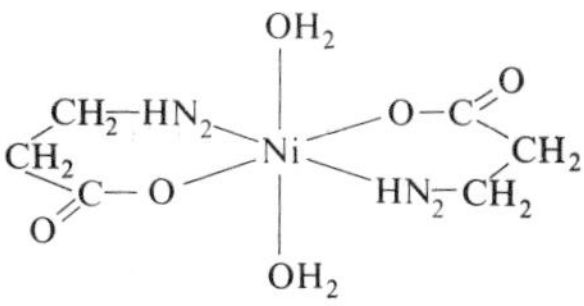

XLV

The tetrahedral, ionic structure $[Ni(NH_3)_4]^{2+}2X^-$ was originally proposed for the tetrammine nickel compounds on the basis of their paramagnetism, but many of these have since been shown to be molecular octahedral compounds; those which have been examined by X-ray methods include the ammines $[Ni(NH_3)_4(NO_2)_2]$ and $[Ni(NH_3)_4(NCS)_2]$, the corresponding pyridine compounds $[Ni(py)_4Cl_2]$, $[Ni(py)_4Br_2]$ and $[Ni(py)_4(NCS)_2]$ and the ethylenediamine derivative $[Ni(en)_2(NCS)_2]$.

Nickel acetylacetonate, which is precipitated from aqueous solution as the dihydrate, can be readily dehydrated to a deep green, paramagnetic, anhydrous compound, $Ni(acac)_2$, long thought to be an example of tetrahedral nickel(II); however, it is now known that in the solid state, this compound forms octahedrally co-ordinated trimers (XLVI), in which some of the oxygen atoms form bridges; magnetic, spectroscopic and molecular weight measurements show that the trimeric structure is preserved in solution and is also adopted by anhydrous nickel benzoylacetonate, though some related compounds, such as the dipivaloylmethanate (XLVII), adopt the low-spin diamagnetic configuration, and are presumably square planar.

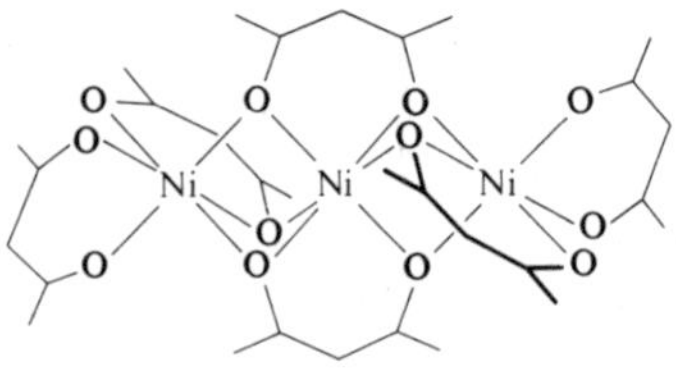

XLVI 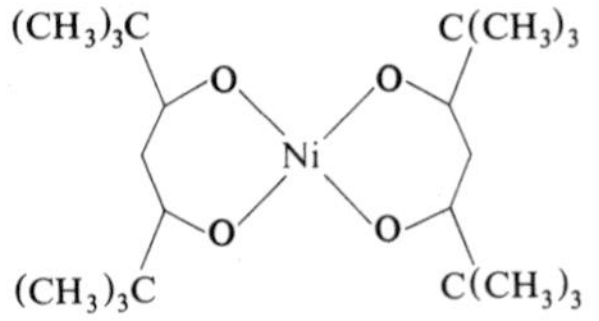 XLVII

Other examples of square-planar nickel include the complex cyanide ion, $[Ni(CN)_4]^{2-}$, the phthalocyanine (see p. 153) and compounds with sulphur atoms as donors, such as the dithiooxalate and the complex formed with thiosemicarbazide (XLIX).

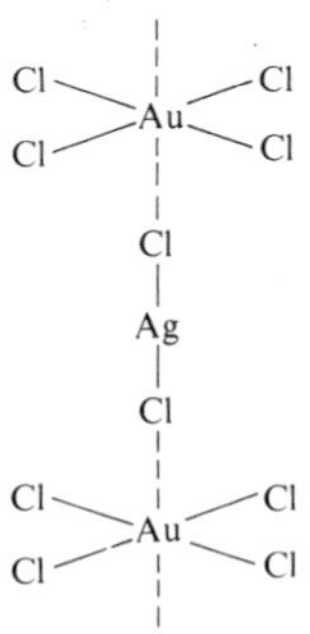

XLVIII 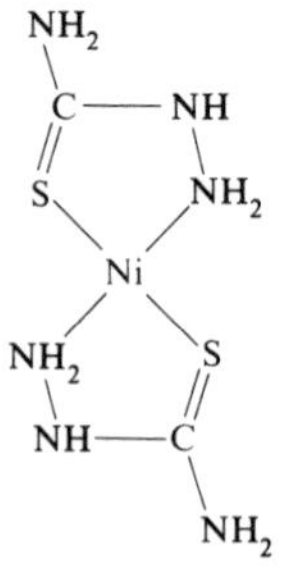 XLIX 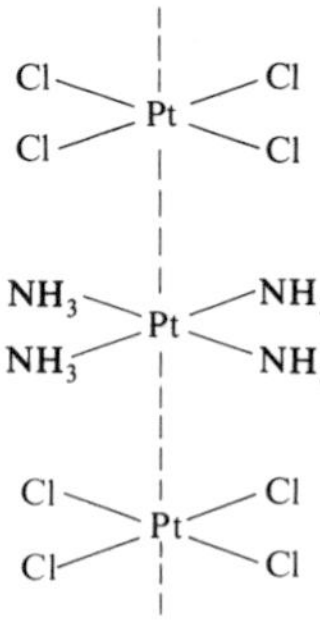 L

In solid nickel dimethylglyoxime (Fig. XVII, Chapter VII) individual square-planar molecules contain remarkably short hydrogen bonds, and are packed in columns with the nickel atoms forming long chains (Fig. XVIII, Chapter VII); the palladium and platinum compounds are similar but with more normal hydrogen bonds, and differ from the copper compound, which forms O-bridged dimers as already described. In nickel dimethylglyoxime, there appears to be some interaction between the nickel atoms in the long chains (Ni—Ni 3·25 Å) since the reflectance spectrum of the solid contains an absorption band which is missing in solution. Unusual absorption bands are observed in some other compounds with columnar structures, such as Magnus's green salt (L), but the reason for this is obscure, as the spectra of the isostructural compounds $[Pd(NH_3)_4]^{2+}$ $[PtCl_4]^{2-}$ and $[Cu(NH_3)_4]^{2+}$ $[PtCl_4]^{2-}$, are normal.

With the ligand *o*-phenylene-bisdimethylarsine ("diarsine") nickel and palladium form isomorphous iodides, $[M(diarsine)_2]I_2$. These compounds are diamagnetic and X-ray analysis of the palladium compound has shown that the metal atom is surrounded by four coplanar arsenic atoms (Pd—As 2·38 Å) and two iodine atoms in the fifth and sixth positions, but at very long distances (Pd—I 3·52 Å). This arrangement recalls the distorted octahedral arrangement common in compounds of copper(II). A somewhat similar situation arises in the compound $CsAuCl_3$, apparently a complex halide of gold(II), but shown by its isomorphism with the compound $Cs_2AgAuCl_6$ to contain gold(I) and gold(III). In the solid compound the gold(I) or silver atoms are linearly co-ordinated in MCl_2^- ions and the gold(III) square co-ordinated in $AuCl_4^-$ ions. However, these two types of ions are so arranged that the gold(III) atoms have an elongated octahedral environment (Au—4Cl 2·42 Å; Au—2Cl 3·13 Å) (XLVIII).

The inner complexes which nickel forms with salicylaldehyde and its *N*-derivatives, such as salicylaldoxime and the salicylaldimines, present an interesting stereochemical study. The salicylaldehyde complex itself precipitates from solution as dihydrate, from which a green, paramagnetic, anhydrous complex can be obtained; the structure of this is unknown, though preliminary X-ray data show that there are twelve nickel atoms in the unit cell, suggesting that it is probably an octahedral trimer like the acetylacetonate. The *N*-derivatives are normally anhydrous and are polymorphic, several of them being known in both diamagnetic and paramagnetic forms. In no case has the crystal structure of a paramagnetic isomer been determined, but these forms are thought to be octahedral polymers; the diamagnetic forms of nickel salicylaldoxime and several of the *N*-alkyl salicylaldimines have been examined by X-ray analysis; most form square-planar molecules and, in some instances, these are packed in columnar form with the nickel atoms of successive molecules forming long chains through the crystal; this type of packing occurs, for example, in one form of the *N*-methylsalicylaldimine, which is isomorphous with the corresponding compounds of copper(XXXII) and palladium.

The straight chain *N*-alkylsalicylaldimines are green, diamagnetic and square planar in the solid state, but give paramagnetic solutions, with μ_{eff} about 2 Bohr magnetons, even in non-donor solvents. It has been found that the compounds are associated in these solutions and the rather low magnetic moments are thought to arise from equilibrium mixtures of the square-planar diamagnetic monomers and paramagnetic octahedral polymers, analogous to that formed by the acetylacetonate. When the alkyl groups have branched chains, the compounds, which have a very similar green colour, are paramagnetic, and in the solid state the molecules are distorted out of the plane towards a tetrahedral structure; the extent of this distortion increases from iso-propyl to *tert*-butyl-salicylaldimines. These branched chain compounds are paramagnetic ($\mu \sim 3{\cdot}3$), but in solution the magnetic moments are lowered ($\mu \sim 2$) due to the establishment of equilibrium between monomeric tetrahedral and square-planar forms. Under some circumstances all three forms can exist in equilibrium together.

Some phosphine complexes of nickel(II) are also tetrahedral, for example, the bis(triphenylphosphine)nickel(II) halides, but others such as bis(triethylphosphine)nickel(II) nitrate are square planar; the stereochemistry adopted depends on both the phosphine concerned and the co-ordinated anion. Tetrahedral stereochemistry also occurs in the complex halide ions, NiX_4^{2-}.

COBALT

The Co^{3+} ion forms an enormous number of extremely stable complexes, the octahedral stereochemistry of which was firmly established sixty years ago by the classical researches of Werner; in almost all of these compounds, the ion has the low-spin configuration, with the six *d*-electrons paired in the lower *d*-orbitals. The stereochemistry of the d^7-ion, Co^{2+}, has proved much more difficult to interpret; most of the complexes of cobalt(II) are of the high-spin type and so labile that their co-ordination numbers change from solvent to solvent, and replacement of some or all of the co-ordinated ligands by solvent molecules is a common feature of their solution chemistry; it is only during the last few years that a deeper understanding of magnetic properties and absorption spectra has made it possible to make reliable assignments of stereochemistry to cobalt(II) compounds without X-ray analysis.

Like d^9-ions, high-spin d^7-ions have an unsymmetrical electron distribution in an octahedral environment; but in d^7-ions, the asymmetry occurs in the inner, d_ϵ-shell and not in the outer d_γ-shell, and so smaller deviations from octahedral symmetry could be expected than are observed in copper(II) compounds (LI). In a tetrahedral environment, however, the electron distribution is symmetrical and perfectly symmetrical complexes could be expected with four similar ligands (LII). We may also note that in a square-planar complex, there must still be one unpaired electron, and magnetic moments of the order of 2β could be expected (LIII).

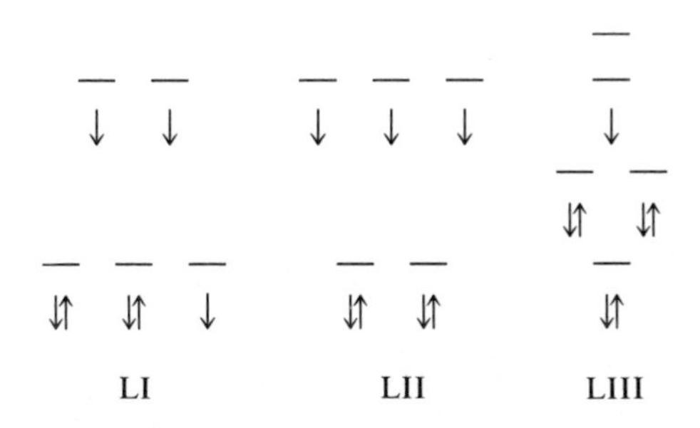

For many years the problem of the stereochemistry of cobalt(II) has centred on the existence of two isomers of the compounds CoX_2L_2 (where X is a halogen or pseudo-halogen and L is water or a nitrogenous base); many of these compounds have been obtained in two forms, one deep blue or green and the other lilac or pink; one form is always more stable than the other at room temperature, but interconversion may occur on heating; thus the pyridine compound $CoCl_2py_2$ is precipitated from alcoholic solution as a lilac powder, which on heating, turns deep blue at about 120°C. In some other cases, for example, $CoCl_2(NH_3)_2$, the blue form is the one which is stable at room temperature.

At different times various stereochemical relationships have been proposed for these pairs of isomers. Following Werner's demonstration that the two forms of $PdCl_2(NH_3)_2$ were *cis*- and *trans*-forms of a square-planar compound, this type of isomerism was attributed to the corresponding cobalt(II) compounds. However, by incorporating Co^{2+} in various host lattices, it has been shown that the colour of the compounds is blue when the cobalt atom has a tetrahedral environment, and pink when its environment is octahedral, and this suggested that the blue isomers had a tetrahedral structure, the lilac being perhaps square planar. There are, however, differences in magnetic properties between these isomers: the blue compounds usually have magnetic moments about $4{\cdot}5\beta$, and the lilac compounds about $4{\cdot}9\beta$; these are both rather above the spin-only value of $3{\cdot}88\beta$ expected for a d^7-ion, but neither agrees with the value of about $1{\cdot}7\beta$ expected from the valence-bond interpretation of the bonding of a d^7-ion in a square-planar complex (LIII). On the other hand, this approach would predict three unpaired electrons in both octahedral, outer orbital (LVI) and tetrahedral complexes (LV), and on this basis it has been proposed that, whereas the blue isomers are tetrahedral, the lilac and pink compounds are octahedral polymers.

	3d					4s	4p			4d					
LIV	⇅	⇅	⇅	↓	⇅	[⇅	⇅	⇅]							square
LV	⇅	⇅	↓	↓	↓	[⇅	⇅	⇅	⇅]						tetrahedral
LVI	⇅	⇅	↓	↓	↓	[⇅	⇅	⇅	⇅	⇅	⇅]				octahedral

This conclusion has since been confirmed by the X-ray analysis of the lilac form of $CoCl_2py_2$, which has been found to have an octahedral polymeric structure like that of $CdCl(NH_3)_2$ (X), each cobalt atom being surrounded by four chlorine atoms at a distance of 2·49 Å and two nitrogen atoms at 2·14 Å (compare the distances in the elongated octahedral polymeric $CuCl_2py_2$, p. 66). Although the blue form of $CoCl_2py_2$ has not been examined by X-ray analysis, the corresponding compounds, $CoCl_2$aniline$_2$ and $CoCl_2$*p*-toluidine$_2$, of which the blue isomers are the stable form, have been shown to be tetrahedral; a tetrahedral environment of the cobalt atom has also been demonstrated in the deep blue compounds, $K_2[Co(NCS)_4].4H_2O$, $[N(CH_3)_4][CoCl_4]$, $Cs_2[CoCl_4]$ and Cs_3CoCl_5, the last of which contains tetrahedral $[CoCl_4]^{-2}$ ions together with Cs^+ and free Cl^- ions.

In addition to the lilac form of $CoCl_2py_2$ X-ray analysis has also established octahedral co-ordination of Co^{2+} in the pink hydrate $CoCl_2.2H_2O$, which has a similar polymeric structure (Co—4Cl, 2·46 Å; Co—2O, 2·04 Å). Other pink compounds in which the cobalt atom has been found to have an octahedral environment are bis(acetylacetonato)diaquocobalt(II) (LVII), cobalt(II) acetate tetrahydrate and dichlorotetrapyridine cobalt(II), the last two of which are isostructural with the corresponding nickel(II) compounds. All of these have magnetic moments of about 4·9β, the difference of about 0·4β from the moments of the tetrahedral species being attributed to the addition of a larger orbital contribution over and above the spin-only moment for three unpaired electrons.

While magnetic properties are valuable in distinguishing between tetrahedral and octahedral complexes of cobalt(II), their usefulness is limited by the small differences in the magnetic moments and the rather wide range observed for each stereochemistry: experimentally observed moments range continuously from about 4·1β to above 5·0β. The absorption spectra of these compounds provide a more valuable analytical tool as they differ markedly from one stereochemistry to the other: the octahedral complexes are characterized by a group of three or four overlapping bands of low intensity (molar extinction coefficient ϵ below 50), usually in the green region (near 500 mμ); the spectra of the tetrahedral compounds also consist of a group of overlapping bands, usually at slightly longer wavelengths (near 600 mμ), but of very much greater intensity ($\epsilon = 200$–2000). As a result of this difference in intensity, very small amounts of tetrahedral species can be observed in the presence of large excesses of the octahedral compounds and the visual observation of a deep blue or green colour is possibly the most critical test for tetrahedral stereochemistry in cobalt(II) compounds.

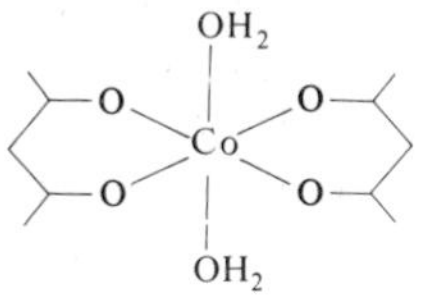

LVII 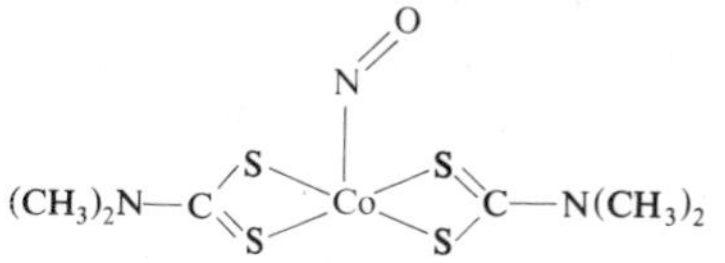 LVIII

A few cobalt(II) compounds are known with much lower magnetic moments, usually in the range 2·0–2·5β; they are mostly brown and are derivatives of phthalocyanin, porphyrins and Schiff's bases; they are generally assumed to be square-planar complexes, though it has recently been found that bis(*N*-methylsalicylaldiminato)cobalt(II) is isomorphous with the zinc compound, and is a 5:co-ordinate dimer (XV). Five co-ordination of cobalt(II) is also observed in terpyridyl cobalt(II) chloride and in nitrosyl bis(dimethyldithiocarbamato)cobalt(II) (LVIII).

Despite the existence of many compounds with co-ordination number five, particularly of copper(II) and zinc, it is clear that the stereochemistry of the majority of compounds of the transition metals falls into one of three main groups: tetrahedral, octahedral or square planar. However, it is not nearly so clear what factors determine the stereochemistry adopted in any particular case.

Tetrahedral complexes appear to be restricted almost entirely to halides and ligands in which the donor atoms are large or of high polarizability such as phosphorus and sulphur. In the case of complexes of the type MX_2(2-methylpyridine)$_2$ (where X = halogen), there is direct evidence that a monomeric tetrahedral structure may be adopted in preference to an octahedral polymeric one for steric reasons, and the change in structure of the *N*-alkyl-salicylaldimine complexes of nickel(II) from square planar in the solid state to presumably tetrahedral in solution, lends support to this view, since these are just those compounds in which it is apparent from the interatomic distances in the crystal that the alkyl groups are responsible for considerable overcrowding in the planar molecules.

The change from octahedral stereochemistry to square planar is more complicated as it is usually accompanied by a change in spin multiplicity. This allows the *d*-electrons to occupy lower energy levels in a square complex than in an octahedral one, and some energetic stabilization of the square structure must arise in this way; but it seems likely that, unless the orbital separation energies are very big, most of this gain will be offset by the need to supply the appropriate spin-pairing energy. The larger orbital separation energies usual in the elements of the second and third long periods probably explain the almost invariable choice of square-planar structures in complexes of the d^8-ions Pd^{2+}, Pt^{2+} and Au^{3+}, but in the first transition series some other explanation is necessary, particularly as a high ligand field is no guarantee of a square-planar structure. Thus, although the $[Ni(CN)_4]^{2-}$ ion is square planar, the nitrite ion which is usually placed next to cyanide in the spectrochemical series gives an octahedral, high-spin complex $[Ni(NO_2)_6]^{4-}$; furthermore, numerous square-planar complexes are formed by copper(II), although in this case the unchanged spin multiplicity offers no energetic compensation.

Most of the square-planar complexes of copper(II), nickel(II) and cobalt(II) are formed by ligands in which the donor atom forms part of a conjugated system, thus suggesting that rather than the square-planar structure arising as a result of spin pairing due to high ligand fields, it may be imposed by the ligand, possibly due to the occurrence of conjugation throughout the whole system when all the donor atoms are coplanar or to the possibility of additional stabilization due to π-bonding between the ligand and the metal d_{xz}- and d_{yz}-orbitals. In this context it is noteworthy that donor atoms such as sulphur or phosphorus, which have vacant *d*-orbitals, can also lead to the formation of square-planar complexes.

HIGH CO-ORDINATION NUMBERS

Co-ordination numbers greater than six are extremely rare in compounds of first row transition metals. Seven co-ordination has been observed in crystalline ethylenediamine-tetraacetate complexes of manganese(II) and iron(III), the complex ions being $[Mn.EDTA^{4-}.H_2O]^{2-}$ and $[Fe.EDTA^{4-}.H_2O]^{-}$. In the complex formed by titanium tetrachloride and *o*-phenylenebis(dimethylarsine) (LIX) the metal atom is 8:co-ordinate (LX), but the Ti—As distance of 2·71 Å is about 0·5 Å longer than in 6:co-ordinate arsine complexes and the Ti—Cl distance of 2·46 Å is about 0·1 Å longer than the metal chlorine distance in the octahedral ions $TiCl_6^{2-}$ or $GeCl_6^{2-}$. The 8:co-ordinate complex can thus be regarded as "overcrowded".

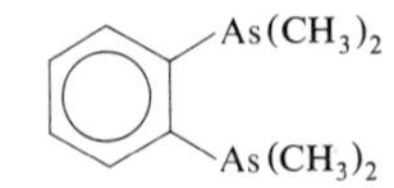

LIX 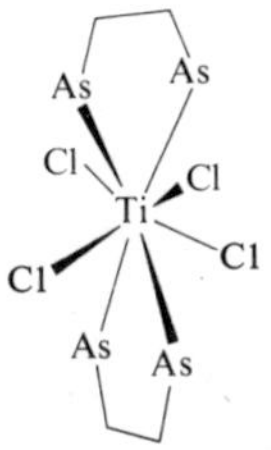 LX

Co-ordination numbers of seven and eight are comparatively common in complex compounds of second and third row transition metals. Seven co-ordinate complex fluoride ions occur in the compounds K_3ZrF_7, K_2NbF_7, K_2TaF_7 and in K_3UF_7 and $K_3UO_2F_5$. In K_3ZrF_7, K_3UF_7 and $K_3UO_2F_5$ the complex ion is pentagonal bipyramidal (LXI) but in K_2NbF_7 and K_2TaF_7 the seventh fluorine atom is added to one of the rectangular faces of a trigonal prism (LXII).

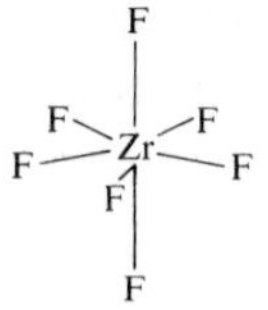

LXI 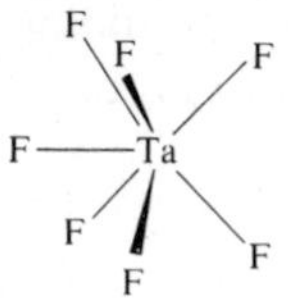 LXII

Two shapes are commonly found in 8:co-ordinate complexes. In the complex cyanides of molybdenum(IV) and tungsten(IV) the shape of the $Mo(CN)_8^{4-}$ or $W(CN)_8^{4-}$ ion (LXIII) is similar to that in the titanium tetrachloride-diarsine complex (LX); this shape is often referred to as

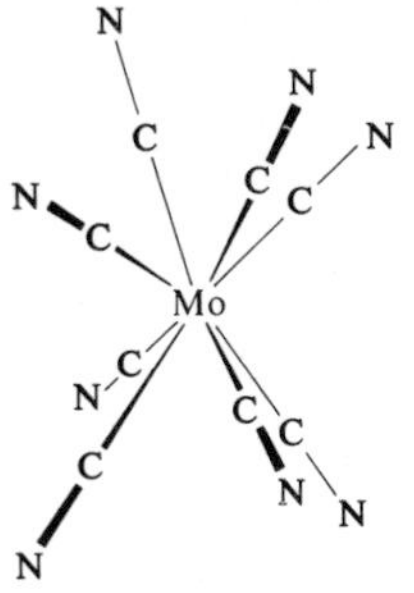

LXIII 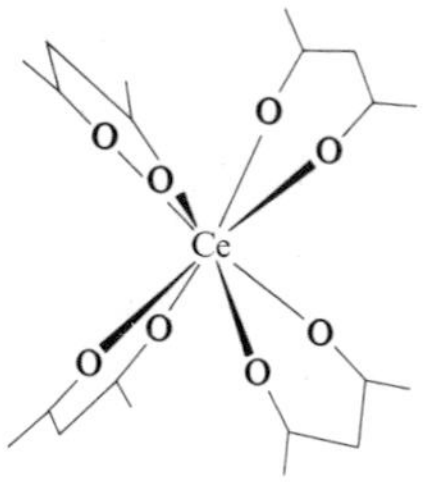 LXIV

a bisdisphenoid and is also observed in the complex ion $Zr(C_2O_4)_4^{4-}$ and in the neutral molecule tetrakis(dibenzoylmethanato)cerium(IV). In the corresponding tetrakis(acetylacetonato)cerium(IV) and in the zirconium and thorium compounds, however, the donor atoms are placed at the corners of a square Archimedean antiprism (LXIV).

METAL–METAL BONDS

In copper(II) acetate hydrate (XXXIV) the acetate bridges hold two copper atoms at a distance about the same as that in metallic copper and it is possible to interpret the magnetic interaction of these copper atoms in terms of a Cu—Cu bond, though it has been found that in this particular case the bond energy is extremely small. There is, however, a number of other compounds, particularly of A-subgroup metals, in which metal–metal bonds are an important feature of the structures of the compounds. The simplest of these compounds are the salts of the ion $W_2Cl_9^{3-}$, obtained by electrolytic reduction of tungstates in hydrochloric acid solution. The complex ion is formed by two octahedra sharing a face (LXV) and the W—W distance of 2·41 Å is 0·3 Å shorter than that in metallic tungsten. The importance of the W—W bond is shown by comparison with the corresponding $Cr_2Cl_9^{3-}$ ion, which has the same structure but with a Cr—Cr distance of 3·12 Å, 0·6 Å greater than that in the metal.

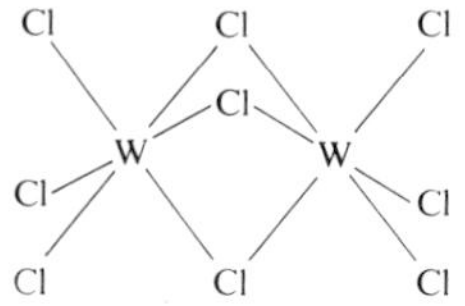

Cl Cl Cl
Cl
W W
Cl Cl
Cl Cl Cl

LXV

Complex halides of trivalent rhenium, such as $CsReCl_4$, have been known for many years and have unusually low solubilities; they are diamagnetic and have been assumed to contain the tetrahedral low-spin d^4-ion $ReCl_4^-$. A recent structure determination on $CsReCl_4$, however, has revealed a trimeric $Re_3Cl_{12}^{3-}$ ion with a triangle of rhenium atoms linked by Re—Re bonds (LXVI). The Re—Re distances are 2·50 Å (compared with 2·75 Å in the metal), in-plane Re—Cl 2·60, out-of-plane Re—Cl 2·35 and bridging Re—Cl 2·43 Å. The Re—Cl distance in the regular octahedral ion $ReCl_6^{2-}$ is 2·37 Å, thus suggesting that the terminal in-plane Re—Cl links in the trimeric ion are rather weak. It is thus not very surprising that an ion $Re_3Cl_{11}^{2-}$, formed by removing one of these terminal chlorine atoms, should occur in another complex halide and that it should be possible to replace all three terminal chlorine atoms by diethylphenyl-phosphine to form a trimeric neutral complex (LXVII).

LXVI LXVII

A more elaborate framework of metal–metal bonds is found in some complexes of molybdenum, niobium and tantalum in their lower oxidation states. By heating molybdenum in phosgene or by the action of heat on molybdenum(III) chloride, a yellow residue is formed of empirical formula $MoCl_2$. This compound is soluble in alcohol but only one-third of the chlorine is precipitated from solution by silver ions. The formula has been shown to be $[Mo_6Cl_8]^{4+}4Cl^-$, and the four chloride ions can be replaced by Br^-, I^-, NO_3^-, etc. There is a similar bromide, Mo_6Br_{12}, and crystal structure analysis has shown that the Mo_6X_8 group is based on an octahedron of molybdenum atoms surrounded by halogen atoms at the corners of a cube (LXVIII). The Mo—Mo distances are 2·6 Å (compared with 2·73 Å in the metal) and the Mo—Cl distances 2·56 Å.

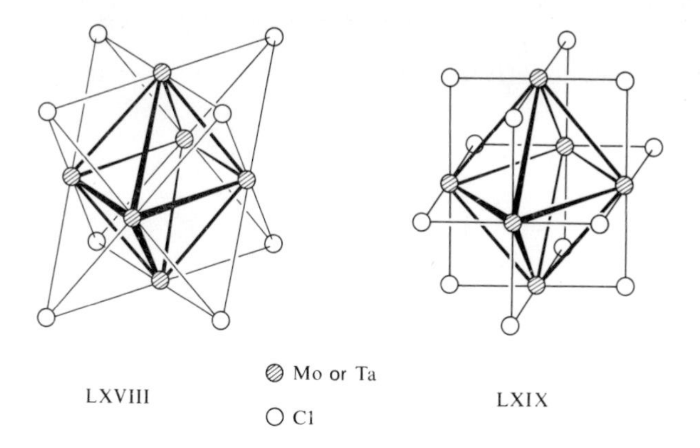

LXVIII LXIX

A rather similar structure (LXIX) has been proposed for the $Ta_6Cl_{12}^{2+}$ unit in Ta_6Cl_{14}, which readily loses two chlorine atoms as Cl^- ions.

The occurrence of metal–metal bonds of this type appears to be a feature of A-subgroup metals forming compounds in unusually low oxidation states, and has been interpreted in terms of oxidation potentials and electronegativities and also in terms of molecular orbitals. Metal–metal bonds are also a common feature of metal carbonyl and π-complex chemistry (Chapter VI).

FURTHER READING

Chemical Society *Tables of Interatomic Distances and Configuration in Molecules and Ions*, London (1958); Supplement, London (1965).

WELLS, A. F., *Structural Inorganic Chemistry*, 3rd ed., Oxford (1962).

WHEATLEY, P. J., *The Determination of Molecular Structure*, Oxford (1959).

ADDISON, C. C. and LOGAN, N., Anhydrous metal nitrates, *Advances Inorg. Chem., Radiochem.* **6**, 72 (1964).

BOOTH, G., Complexes of the transition metals with phosphines, arsines and stibines, *Advances Inorg. Chem., Radiochem.* **6**, 1 (1964).

COLLMAN, J. P., Reactions of metal acetylacetonates, *Angew. Chem.* **77**, 154 (1965).

DUNITZ, J. D. and ORGEL, L. E., Stereochemistry of ionic solids, *Advances Inorg. Chem., Radiochem.* **2**, 1 (1960).

GRIFFITH, W. P., Cyanide complexes of the transition metals, *Quart. Rev.* **16**, 188 (1962).

HARRIS, C. M. and LIVINGSTONE, S. E., Spin-paired complexes of nickel(II), palladium(II), platinum(II) and gold(III) with high covalency, *Rev. Pure App. Chem.* **12**, 16 (1962).

KATO, M., JONASSEN, H. B. and FANNING, J. C., Copper(II) complexes with subnormal magnetic moments, *Chem. Rev.* **64**, 99 (1964).

LEWIS, J., Metal–metal interaction in transition-metal complexes, *Pure and Applied Chem.* **10**, 11 (1965).

LIVINGSTONE, S. E., Metal complexes of ligands containing sulphur, selenium or tellurium as donor atoms, *Quart. Rev.* **19**, 386 (1965).

MILLER, J. R., Recent advances in the stereochemistry of nickel, palladium and platinum, *Advances Inorg. Chem., Radiochem.* **4**, 133 (1962).

SCHAEFFER, H. and SCHNERING, H. G., Metal–metal bonds in lower halides, oxides and oxide–halides of heavier transition metals, *Angew. Chem.* **76**, 833 (1964).

VENANZI, L. M., Complexes with quadridentate phosphorus- and arsenic-containing ligands, *Angew. Chem.* **76**, 621 (1964).

WEST, B. O., The chemistry of inner complexes, *Rev. Pure App. Chem.* **10**, 207 (1960).

CHAPTER IV

THE STABILITY OF COMPLEX SALTS

COMPLEX compounds are often described qualitatively as "stable" or "unstable"; the cobaltammines, for example, and many of the complex cyanides are obviously stable in the sense that they can be kept indefinitely without decomposition and, in solution, fail to give the normal analytical reactions of their constituents. Other compounds, like many of the hydrocarbon and carbonyl complexes, are very readily decomposed by heat or hydrolysed by water or are photosensitive.

In this chapter we shall not be primarily concerned with stability in this sense, but with the numerous co-ordination compounds of metal cations which, to a greater or lesser extent, undergo reactions in which one ligand replaces another reversibly. In particular, the most familiar example of this behaviour is the reaction of complex salts with a solvent (nearly always water) to form the solvated (hydrated) metal ion and free ligands:

$$ML_n + nH_2O \rightleftharpoons M(OH_2)_n + nL\dagger$$

The reverse of this reaction represents the formation of a complex ion from its constituents in aqueous solution and must proceed by a stepwise replacement of co-ordinated water molecules by ligand molecules or ions:

$$M(OH_2)_n + L \rightleftharpoons M(OH_2)_{n-1}L + OH_2$$
$$M(OH_2)_{n-1}L + L \rightleftharpoons M(OH_2)_{n-2}L_2 + OH_2 \ldots$$
$$\ldots M(OH_2)L_{n-1} + L \rightleftharpoons ML_n + OH_2$$

For each step in this process there is an equilibrium constant defined by the expressions:

$$k_1 = \frac{[M(OH_2)_{n-1}L]}{[M(OH_2)_n] \times [L]}$$
$$k_2 = \frac{[M(OH_2)_{n-2}L_2]}{[M(OH_2)_{n-1}L] \times [L]} \ldots$$
$$\ldots k_n = \frac{[ML_n]}{[M(OH_2)L_{n-1}] \times [L]}$$

†Throughout this chapter the charges on the metal atoms and the ligands are omitted in general equations so as to avoid confusion.

The constants $k_1, k_2, \ldots, k_n$ are the successive stability constants of the system. For statistical reasons and because of the repulsion of a co-ordinated ligand for an incoming ligand of similar type the values of these constants nearly always decrease in the order

$$k_1 > k_2 > k_3 > \ldots k_n$$

as in the examples in Table 1.

TABLE 1. SUCCESSIVE AND OVERALL FORMATION CONSTANTS†

System	$\log k_1$	$\log k_2$	$\log k_3$	$\log k_4$	$\log k_5$	$\log k_6$	Overall
Hg^{2+}/Br^-	8·9	7·9	2·3	1·7			$\log \beta_4 = 20{\cdot}8$
Cd^{2+}/I^-	2·4	1·0	1·6	1·1			$\log \beta_4 = 6{\cdot}1$
Ni^{2+}/NH_3	2·8	2·0	1·7	1·3	0·7	0·4	$\log \beta_6 = 8{\cdot}9$
Zn^{2+}/en	6·0	4·8	2·2				$\log \beta_3 = 13{\cdot}0$
Co^{2+}/glycinate	4·6	3·8	2·4				$\log \beta_3 = 10{\cdot}8$
Th^{4+}/oxinate	10·5	10·0	9·5	8·9			$\log \beta_4 = 38{\cdot}9$

†Data throughout this chapter are taken from *Stability Constants*, published by the Chemical Society, London (1964). For many systems numerous conflicting results are given, and there is no uniform basis of solvent conditions for comparison. Where possible, data have been chosen corresponding to ionic strength zero, but the choice has been made arbitrarily, and some of the doubt about the validity of the data eliminated by rounding off to one decimal point.

The product of the successive stability constants:

$$k_1 \times k_2 \times k_3 \ldots k_n = \frac{[ML_n]}{[M(OH_2)_n] \times [L]^n} = \beta$$

is the overall stability constant of the system and is commonly used as a general guide to the stability of the complex in this sense.

Values of the overall stability constant may cover a very wide range: for extremely stable complexes, such as the ferrocyanide ion, $[Fe(CN)_6]^{4-}$, values greater than 10^{30} may occur and for very unstable complexes β may even be less than unity; on account of this wide range the values of the constants are frequently quoted on a logarithmic scale. As a rough guide, a value of $\log \beta$ greater than about 8 represents what we should normally think of as a "stable" complex.

THE DETERMINATION OF STABILITY CONSTANTS

In principle stability constants are determined by studying the concentrations of the various species present in a wide range of equilibrium mixtures containing the metal ion and the ligand in different proportions.

For a reasonably stable complex the dominant species present with a given ligand–metal ratio are those with the nearest integral ratios above and below; for example, for a ligand–metal ratio of 2·7 : 1, the species predominantly present are ML_2 and ML_3. It is thus possible, by adjusting the ligand–metal ratio to examine experimentally successive steps in the process of complex formation.

First, however, it is necessary to establish the number of steps in the equilibrium, that is the maximum number of ligands which can be attached to each metal atom. This is not necessarily the same as the co-ordination number or the number of ligands attached to the metal in any solid compound which may be isolated, as in solution some of the ligands may be displaced by the solvent, particularly if this is water.

The stoichiometry of the system under the conditions of the experiment is determined by Job's method of continuous variations: some property is chosen which changes as complex formation takes place (for example, colour intensity, pH or an electrode potential) and plotted as ordinate against the concentrations of the metal cation and the ligand put into solution, the sum of these concentrations being kept constant. If no complex formation occurs the result will be a straight line (Fig. 1), but if complex formation occurs a curve will be obtained (Fig. 2); the difference between this curve and the straight line of Fig. 1 is then plotted and will be found to represent two intersecting straight lines (or, if the complexes formed are of low stability, it may become rounded) (Fig. 3); the ligand–metal ratio represented by the point of intersection is the ratio in the highest complex formed in solution and hence also the number of steps in the process.

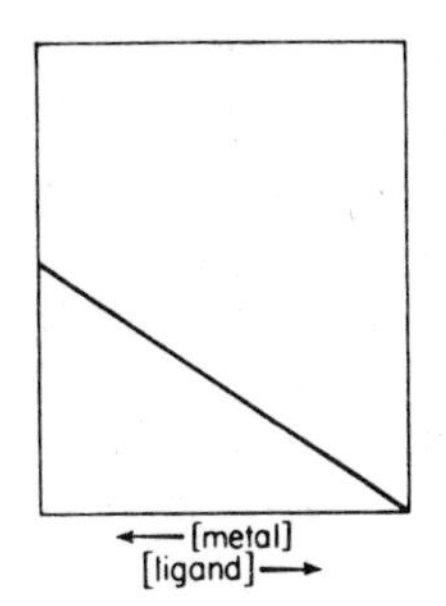

FIG. 1. No complex formation.

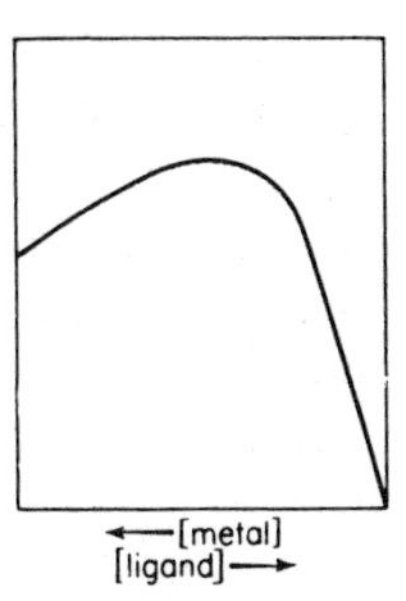

FIG. 2. Curve shows complex formation.

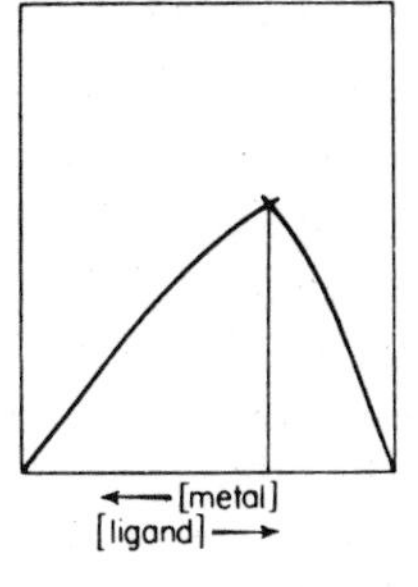

FIG. 3. Intersection shows 2 : 1 complex.

The first step in complex formation may now be examined by investigating the variation of a suitable physical property over an appropriate range of concentrations of metal and ligand (but the value of this property representing completion of the first step in complex formation will have to be found by trial and error as it will not correspond exactly to the value observed for a 1 : 1 ratio).

In order to overcome the difficulties introduced by variations in the ionic strength of the medium, it is usual to carry out these experiments at an arbitrary ionic strength, controlled by the addition of a non-complexing electrolyte, such as sodium perchlorate. Thermodynamic equilibrium constants may then be obtained by application of the Debye–Hückel theory or of one of the approximation formulae derived from it; such formulae are, however, not applicable at ionic strengths greater than about 0·1. Furthermore the theory is based on the consideration of ions as point charges and many of the ligands used in co-ordination chemistry are of considerable size, so that the only really reliable method for obtaining thermodynamic equilibrium constants is that in which the whole of the measurements are repeated at a series of different ionic strengths and the thermodynamic constants obtained by extrapolation to zero ionic strength.

Though simple in principle, the determination of a whole series of thermodynamic equilibrium constants is, in practice, exceedingly difficult and involves considerable mathematical manipulation. This mathematical treatment will not be discussed here; it is readily available in some detail in Martell and Calvin's recently published book. There is also an excellent introduction, giving copious references to the original literature, in the monograph published by the Chemical Society.

Whilst almost every known physical method of investigating solutions has been applied to the study of complexing equilibria, the most widely used methods fall into two classes.

1. *Optical Methods*

These are usually spectrophotometric and depend on the difference in the colour or absorption spectra of the "free" and complexed ions, either the ligand or the metal being the coloured species, or in some cases the complex formed, which may be much more highly coloured than either of the other species.

Let us suppose that at a selected wavelength the optical density of an aqueous solution of a transition metal salt is three units and that we are examining the first step in complex formation; the optical density of the solution containing a 1 : 1 ratio of ligand to metal is found to be, say, twelve units; if formation of the 1 : 1 complex, ML, is complete under these conditions then an optical density of twelve units corresponds to the colour of this complex, but it is more likely that a small excess of the ligand will have to be added to complete this step in complex formation, so that the optical density of the 1 : 1 complex is really a little higher, perhaps thirteen units; let us guess that this is the right figure.

There are now ten units difference in optical density between the solution of the metal ion and the solution of the complex ML, so that the proportion of "free" and complexed metal ion in any solution of intermediate optical density can be estimated by simple proportion: a solution of optical density ten units, for example, would have seven-tenths of the metal in the complexed form. If then we determine the optical densities of a number of solutions containing various proportions of metal and ligand, we can find the proportion of the metal in the complexed form in each solution; since we know the initial concentrations of the metal and the ligand we can thus calculate the concentration of the complex ML and, by difference, of the "free" metal and ligand and hence obtain the equilibrium constant:

$$k_1 = \frac{[ML]}{[M] \times [L]}$$

If our guess at the optical density of the complex ML is correct the values of k_1 obtained for all the solutions of intermediate optical density will be the same; if the values of k_1 drift upwards or downwards as the ligand–metal ratio changes, this shows that our guess at the optical density of the ML complex was not quite right, so we have to guess again and recalculate the values of k_1; this process is repeated until there is no drift, when the scatter of the values of k_1 gives an idea of the accuracy of the result.

Spectrophotometric methods of measuring colour intensity are of only limited accuracy (about $\pm 1\%$) and as the concentrations of some of the species are obtained by difference this means that this method cannot be used for reactions which are heavily one-sided; if, for instance, complex formation was always at least 99% complete, the optical densities observed would be indistinguishable from those which would be observed if complex formation were 100% complete. The spectrophotometric method is, however, particularly suitable for the study of less-stable complexes, where complex formation approaches completeness only in the presence of a considerable excess of the ligand.

2. *Electrochemical Methods*

Exactly the same principles are applied where an electrochemical method is used as have been described for the spectrophotometric method. The simplest of the electrochemical methods is that in which the concentration of "free" metal is determined in an equilibrium of the type:

$$M + nL \rightleftharpoons ML_n$$

The total concentrations of the metal cation and the ligand are either known or determined by standard analytical methods; the concentration of the "free" metal is determined potentiometrically or polarographically and that of the complexed metal by difference.

Another widely used electrochemical method is that in which the pH of the solution is determined in a competition reaction of the type:

$$M^{m+} + nLH \rightleftharpoons ML_n^{(m-n)+} + nH^+$$

This method can only be applied where the ligand, L, is the anion of a weak acid, so that its co-ordination to the metal atom is accompanied by the release of hydrogen ions; it could not be applied satisfactorily, for example, to the co-ordination of chloride ions, since the conjugate acid of the ligand would be a strong acid and already fully ionized before complex formation took place.

Electrochemical methods have the advantage over spectrophotometric methods of greater sensitivity, but are not suitable for use in any but the most dilute solutions. For the most stable complexes even electrochemical methods are not sufficiently sensitive to allow the determination of the successive complexing constants, but there is some prospect that radiochemical methods may prove suitable. In these cases the overall stability constant can be obtained from the effect of complex formation on the standard electrode potential of the metal:

$$\ln \beta = \frac{nF}{RT} \{E^\circ{}_{\text{aqueous}} - E^\circ{}_{\text{complex}}\}$$

FACTORS AFFECTING STABILITY CONSTANTS

Stability constants vary over a very wide range of values even when we consider only the reaction of a single ligand with a number of metals or a single metal with a variety of ligands. It is thus not possible, as a general rule, to say that any particular metal or any particular ligand forms complexes of outstandingly high or low stability. It is therefore apparent that no single factor can be expected to account for the stabilities of complex salts, but that each case must be considered separately in terms of a subtle blend of contributing factors.

The Electrostatic Factor

Since complex formation is essentially a reaction between a cation and an anion or dipole, the ionic potential (charge–radius ratio) of the cation can be expected to be of paramount importance. It is for this reason that, when a metal forms complexes with the same ligand in more than one valency state, the complexes of the higher valency are nearly always more stable. Table 2 gives some examples of the stability constants of EDTA complexes with metals in two different valency states.

TABLE 2. EFFECT OF VALENCY ON STABILITY OF EDTA COMPLEXES

Cation	V^{2+}	Fe^{2+}	Co^{2+}	Eu^{2+}
log k	12·7	14·3	16·2	7·7
Cation	V^{3+}	Fe^{3+}	Co^{3+}	Eu^{3+}
log k	25·9	25·1	36	17·3

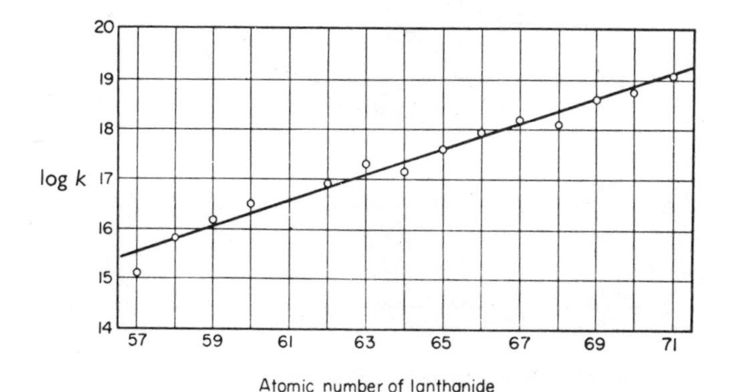

FIG. 4. Stability constants of lanthanide–EDTA complexes.

The ionic potential effect is particularly well illustrated by the regular rise in stability of the lanthanide–EDTA complexes from lanthanum to lutecium due to the "lanthanide contraction", which leads to a steady increase in ionic potential with increasing atomic number (Fig. 4).

Somewhat similar results are observed for complexes of the divalent ions of the transition metals of the first long period. Irving and Williams have shown that the same order of increasing stability:

$$\mathrm{Mn} < \mathrm{Fe} < \mathrm{Co} < \mathrm{Ni} < \mathrm{Cu} > \mathrm{Zn}$$

holds, irrespective of the nature of the ligand (Fig. 2) and this is also the order of decreasing ionic radius (Cu^{2+} smallest). Similar orders had been previously observed by various authors, who also included other, non-transitional ions in their series; but the order in which these "outside" ions appear differs from one ligand to another.

The failure of cations outside the transition metal series to fit into these stability orders always in the same positions, clearly indicates that other factors are involved besides the electrostatic attraction between the cations and the ligands. Probably the most important of these is the need to maintain a correct balance of electrical charge in every part of the complex.

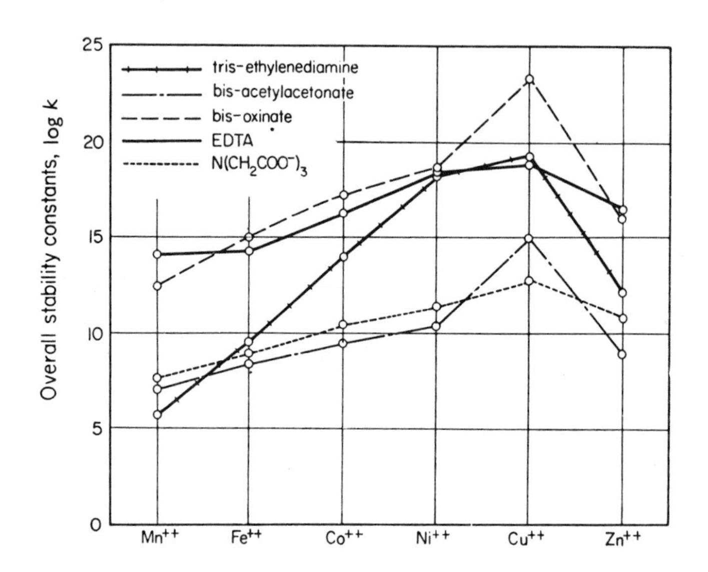

FIG. 5. Stability constants of transition-metal complexes.

Crystal-field Stabilization

The most satisfactory explanation of the Irving–Williams series appears to be that provided by crystal-field theory. In octahedral complexes the d-orbitals are split into two levels, thus:

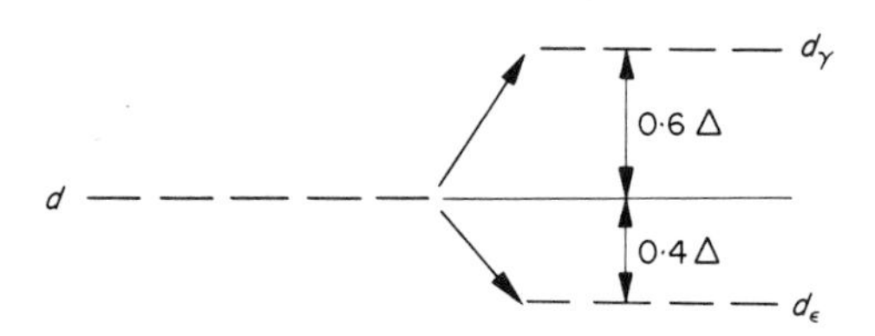

Whenever an electron is placed in a lower, d_ϵ-level the ion is stabilized to the extent of $0{\cdot}4\Delta$ by comparison with the free ion; and whenever an electron is placed in a d_γ-orbital, the ion is destabilized to the extent of $0{\cdot}6\Delta$. The overall stabilization energy (CFSE) of high-spin complexes is as given in Table 3.

TABLE 3. ELECTRONIC STRUCTURES AND CRYSTAL-FIELD STABILIZATION ENERGIES

Ion	d_ϵ			d_γ		CFSE
Ti^{2+}	↓	↓				0·8Δ
V^{2+}	↓	↓	↓			1·2Δ
Cr^{2+}	↓	↓	↓	↓		0·6Δ
Mn^{2+}	↓	↓	↓	↓	↓	0
Fe^{2+}	↓↑	↓	↓	↓	↓	0·4Δ
Co^{2+}	↓↑	↓↑	↓	↓	↓	0·8Δ
Ni^{2+}	↓↑	↓↑	↓↑	↓	↓	1·2Δ
Cu^{2+}	↓↑	↓↑	↓↑	↓↑	↓	0·6Δ
Zn^{2+}	↓↑	↓↑	↓↑	↓↑	↓↑	0

Table 4 shows the observed values of the orbital separation energy Δ and the corresponding crystal-field stabilization energies for some transition metal ions in aquo-complexes.

TABLE 4. Δ AND CFSE FOR IONS $[M(H_2O)_6]^{2+}$ (kcal/g-atom)

M	Mn^{2+}	Fe^{2+}	Co^{2+}	Ni^{2+}	Cu^{2+}
Δ	23	30	27	26	38
CFSE	0	12	22	31	23

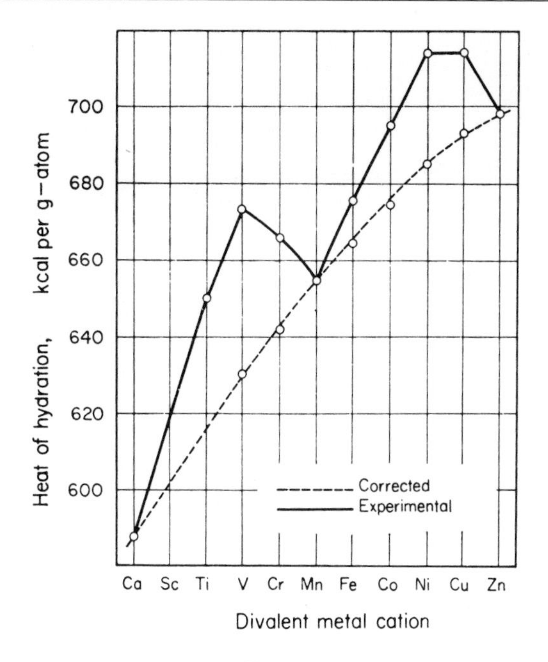

FIG. 6

On the basis of a transition-metal contraction analogous to the lanthanide contraction, a steady rise in stability of complexes could be expected from Mn^{2+} to Zn^{2+}, analogous to that shown in Fig. 4; but superimposed on this general rise would be additional stability due to crystal-field stabilization. Figure 6 shows the heats of hydration of the gaseous ions from Mn^{2+} to Zn^{2+}, from which it can be seen that addition of the crystal-field stabilization energies to the values obtained by interpolation between Mn^{2+} and Zn^{2+} gives remarkably close agreement with observed hydration energies of ions from Fe^{2+} to Cu^{2+}.

Replacement of water molecules by other ligands results in a changed value of Δ and consequently in a different contribution from the crystal-field stabilization energy. In Fig. 7 the enthalpies of formation of tris-ethylenediamine complexes are plotted for the series of cations Mn^{2+} to Zn^{2+}. Here again, the excess stabilities of the complexes of the intermediate ions can be attributed to crystal-field stabilization.

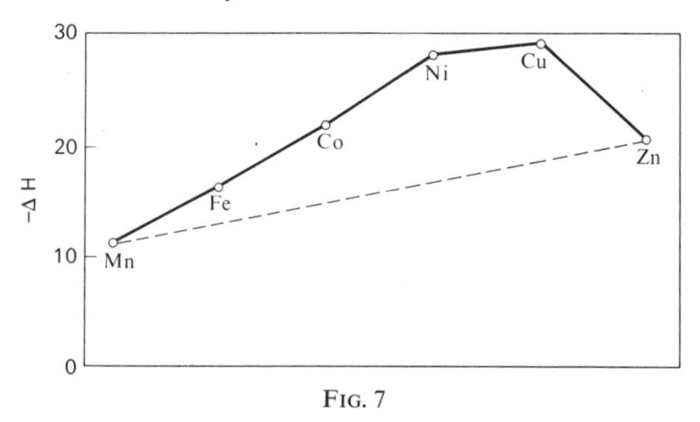

FIG. 7

The excess stability of the nickel complex above that of the aquo ion is about 11 kcal/mole. The value of Δ for the $[Ni\ en_3]^{2+}$ ion is 34 kcal, determined spectroscopically, and this is 8 kcal greater than that for the $[Ni(H_2O)_6]^{2+}$ ion; the extra crystal-field stabilization expected is thus $1{\cdot}2\Delta = 9{\cdot}6$ kcal/mole, which is very close to the observed value of about 11 kcal/mole. Furthermore, the ratio of the additional crystal-field stabilization energies shown in Fig. 7 is very close to the expected ratio of 4:8:12:6.

When the possibility arises of forming low-spin complexes, much greater crystal-field stabilization is possible. This is reflected in the extremely high stability of most cobalt(III) complexes and of low-spin complexes of iron(II) and iron(III). Change of spin of iron(II) complexes leads to a crystal-field stabilization of $2{\cdot}0\Delta$:

	—	—	—	—	—	
Fe^{2+}	⇃↾	↓	↓	↓	↓	CFSE = $0{\cdot}4\Delta$
Fe^{2+}	⇃↾	⇃↾	⇃↾			CFSE = $2{\cdot}4\Delta$

though this will be offset to a large extent by the energy required to enforce spin pairing. The effect of spin pairing on the stability of complexes of divalent ions is shown well by comparison of the overall formation constants of tris-*o*-phenanthroline complexes with those of tris-ethylene-diamine complexes; only the iron(II) *o*-phenanthroline complex has the low-spin configuration.

TABLE 5. OVERALL FORMATION CONSTANTS (LOG β_3) OF *o*-PHENANTHROLINE AND ETHYLENEDIAMINE COMPLEXES

	Mn^{2+}	Fe^{2+}	Co^{2+}	Ni^{2+}	Cu^{2+}	Zn^{2+}	Cd^{2+}
o-phen	7·3	21·3	19·9	23·9	21·4	17·5	14·9
en	5·7	9·7	13·9	18·3	21·0	14·1	12·3

Tris(*o*-phenanthroline)iron(III) is also a low-spin complex and could also be expected to have a very high stability, but the spin-pairing energy of iron(III) is so great—33 kcal/g-atom greater than that of iron(II)—that the low-spin iron(III) complex is actually of lower stability than the iron(II) complex.

$$[Fe(o\text{-phen})_3]^{2+} \qquad \log \beta_3 = 21{\cdot}3$$
$$[Fe(o\text{-phen})_3]^{3+} \qquad \log \beta_3 = 14{\cdot}1$$

In the case of the corresponding cyanide complexes, which are also low spin, the larger value of Δ produced by the cyanide ion allows the crystal-field stabilization energy to outweigh the difference in the pairing energies, and the iron(III) complex is the more stable, though not by a very large margin.

$$[Fe(CN)_6]^{2+} \qquad \log \beta_6 = 24$$
$$[Fe(CN)_6]^{3+} \qquad \log \beta_6 = 31$$

The Principle of Charge Distribution

The process of co-ordination involves the "donation" of a pair of electrons from each ligand to the metal cation. If the bond formed were a perfect covalent bond this would result in the effective transfer of one unit of charge to the metal atom for each co-ordinate bond formed. For a 6:co-ordinate divalent cation this would lead to an accumulation of four negative charges on the metal atom. Such a system would clearly be unstable and it is evident that in stable systems the co-ordinate bonds must have considerable polarity. The extent of electron transfer in any one case depends upon two factors: (a) the ionic potential of the cation; (b) the polarizability of the anion, and as each of these increases so must the amount of negative electrical charge accumulating on the metal atom.

We thus find that stabilities of the complexes of any particular ion increase with increasing polarizability of the ligand, but that there is a limit to this increase because ligands of too high a polarizability would cause the accumulation of too much negative charge on the central atom. For the divalent metal cations from Mn^{2+} to Zn^{2+} stabilities of complexes are found to increase with changing donor atom in the order:

$$F < O < N > S > P$$

donor atoms of the second short period evidently producing too great a transfer of charge to the metal atom.

Such charge transfer may be reduced by a lowering of the co-ordination number as in the ferric-halide complexes where the change of ligand from the octahedral $[FeF_6]^{3-}$ to the tetrahedral $[FeCl_4]^-$ ion. A similar change is shown by the Co^{2+} ion and whereas the Ni^{2+} ion forms octahedral complexes with water or amines as ligands, the complexes in which some of the ligands are substituted phosphines are 4:co-ordinated.

It has been suggested that the balance of polarizability of the ligand and ionic potential of the metal cation is ideally such as to produce electrical neutrality on the metal atom and this is probably near the truth for typical transition-metal ions; it cannot, however, be expected for other types of ion; in particular, ions with inert-gas structures may be expected to offer considerable resistance to the transfer of negative electrical charge, the ideal balance in these instances being that which will leave the cation with its positive charge only slightly lowered.

Irving and Williams propose that the ability to accept transferred charge should be related to the gaseous ionization potentials of the cations, since these are a measure of the energy involved in the reverse process:

$$M_{(gas)} - n\bar{e} = M^{n+}_{(gas)}$$

In practice, however, we are not concerned with gaseous ions but with the behaviour of ions in aqueous solution and a quantity more closely related to the actual processes involved in co-ordination is the standard electrode potential of the metal:

$$M_{(solid)} - n\bar{e} = M^{n+}_{(aqueous)}$$

which is closely related to the ionization potential, but includes terms representing the sublimation energy of the metal and the energy of hydration of the cations.

Table 6 shows the standard electrode potentials of some common metal ions and it can be seen that they fall into three main groups:

(a) Inert gas ions for which $E°$ < about − 1·5 V.
(b) Transition metal ions, $E°$ between about 0 and − 1·0°V.
(c) Noble metal ions of d^8-or d^{10}-structure, $E°$ > about 0·5°V.

TABLE 6. STANDARD ELECTRODE POTENTIALS OF CATIONS (V)

K^+	−2·92	Ti^{2+}	−1·75	Hg^{2+}	+0·85
Na^+	−2·71	V^{2+}	−1·5	Cu^+	+0·52
Ba^{2+}	−2·90	Cr^{2+}	−0·86	Ag^+	+0·80
Sr^{2+}	−2·89	Mn^{2+}	−1·05	Au^+	+1·68
Ca^{2+}	−2·87	Fe^{2+}	−0·44	Au^{3+}	+1·4
Mg^{2+}	−2·34	Co^{2+}	−0·28	Pt^{2+}	+1·2
Be^{2+}	−1·70	Ni^{2+}	−0·25	Pd^{2+}	+0·83
La^{3+}	−2·37	Cu^{2+}	+0·35	Co^{3+}	+0·43
Al^{3+}	−1·67	Zn^{2+}	−0·76	Fe^{3+}	−0·04
TiO^{2+}	−1·0	Cd^{2+}	−0·40	Cr^{3+}	−0·71

These figures refer to the M/M^{n+} couple, but it must be remembered that there may be intermediate oxidation states.

The first group includes all those cations which form their most stable complexes with fluoride ions or ligands with oxygen as donor atom, for example:

$$[Mg(C_2O_4)_2]^{2-}, Be_4O(OOC.CH_3)_6, TiF_6^{2-}$$

even nitrogen usually being too good a donor to form stable complexes. In this group in particular the relative stabilities of complexes with different ligands are very sensitive to slight changes in the balance of ionic potential, ionization potential and polarizability, so that no consistent pattern emerges even in so closely related a series of cations as Mg^{2+}, Ca^{2+} and Sr^{2+}.

The second group includes those ions which form complexes of increasing stability as the ligand atom changes in the order:

$$F < O < N > S > P$$

and as nearly all of the complexes of these ions which have been studied have had oxygen or nitrogen as donor atoms a stability order dependent on the ionic potential of the metal is commonly observed (the Irving–Williams order), but we might expect that this order may no longer hold for complexes in which sulphur or phosphorus atoms act as donors.

The third group consists of the heavier ions with d^{10}- or d^8-structures. These are the ions of the "noble" metals, which have considerable positive electrode potentials and consequently a much greater ability to accept transferred negative charge. They thus form their most stable complexes with ligands of highest polarizability, stabilities varying as the donor atom changes in the order:

$$\mathrm{P} > \mathrm{S} \gg \mathrm{N} > \mathrm{O} > \mathrm{F} \ll \mathrm{Cl} < \mathrm{Br} < \mathrm{I}$$

The ions in this group are also just those which form stable π-complexes with olefins (see Chapter VI) and the abrupt increase in stability of their complexes when the donor atom changes from nitrogen to phosphorus (or arsenic) is taken to indicate that any excessive transfer of charge from the ligand to the metal atom can be relieved by the "back co-ordination" of non-bonding electrons of the metal ion to vacant *d*-orbitals of the donor atom as is shown to occur in some of the metal carbonyls. In this context it is interesting to note that these metals, whose ions are able to adjust to varying degrees of charge transfer in this way are also those which do not form stable carbonyl-type compounds in the zero-valent state.

CHELATION

The stabilities of complexes are greatly increased by the co-ordination of polydentate ligands. The co-ordination of such ligands produces ring structures, the metal atom forming part of the ring; this process is known as chelation (Greek: χηλή, a crab's claw).

The increased stability due to chelation is readily observed by comparing the co-ordinating ability of the anions of dicarboxylic acids and monocarboxylic acids. Carboxylate ions are usually poor ligands forming very unstable complexes; very few complex ions of the type $[M(OOC.R)_4]^{n-}$ or $[M(OOC.R)_6]^{n-}$ can be isolated in complex salts. However, many metals form stable crystalline complex oxalates with $[M(C_2O_4)_2]^{n-}$ or $[M(C_2O_4)_3]^{n-}$ anions and corresponding malonates are also readily formed: in some cases, for example $[Co(C_2O_4)_3]^{3-}$, these complex ions are very stable in solution.

One factor of great importance in chelation is the size of chelate ring produced. This can be seen readily from a comparison of the co-ordinating properties of the first four dicarboxylate anions:

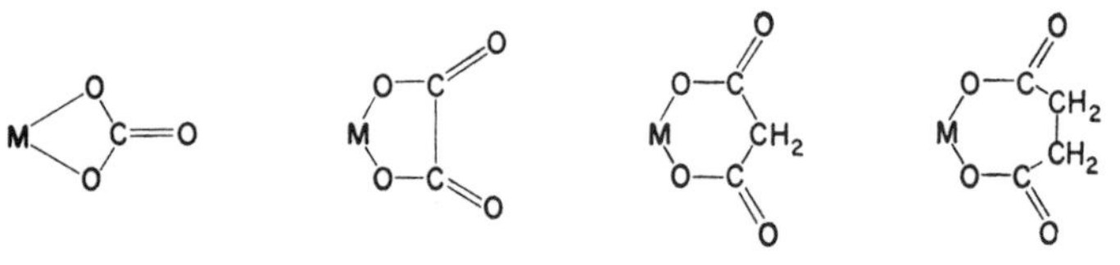

I II III IV

Many metal oxalates and malonates dissolve readily in the presence of a small excess of dicarboxylate anion, with the formation of complex anions containing five- or six-membered chelate rings (II, III), but carbonates and succinates do not dissolve in excess of the alkali metal salts except at very high concentrations, the chelate rings in these cases being four- and seven-membered (I, IV). This effect of ring size is also shown in Table 7 which gives the formation constants for the co-ordination of the first dicarboxylate ion compared with the constant β_2 for co-ordination of two acetate ions.

TABLE 7. FIRST FORMATION CONSTANTS, $\log k_1$, FOR DICARBOXYLATE COMPLEXES COMPARED WITH $\log \beta_2$ FOR ACETATES

Acid	Ring size	Co^{2+}	Ni^{2+}	Cu^{2+}	Zn^{2+}	Cd^{2+}
Oxalic	5	4·5	5·2	6·2	4·8	3·8
Malonic	6	3·7	4·1	5·5	2·8	2·8
Succinic	7	2·2	2·4	3·3	1·8	2·2
Glutaric	8		1·6	2·4	1·6	2·0
Adipic	9		1·6	2·3	1·8	2·1
Acetic	–	1·9	1·8	2·7	2·0	2·2

Considerably greater stabilization of complexes can be achieved by ligands which can occupy still more sites round the metal atom. This is shown particularly well by the series of polyamine ligands of the general formula:

$$NH_2.CH_2.CH_2(NH.CH_2.CH_2)_n\,NH_2$$

When $n = 0$ this is the bidentate ligand ethylene diamine and the series has been extended to the quinquedentate amine, $n = 3$. When any of

TABLE 8. FIRST FORMATION CONSTANTS, $\log k_1$, FOR POLYAMINE COMPLEXES COMPARED WITH $\log \beta_n$ FOR AMMONIA COMPLEXES

No. of N atoms co-ord.	Co^{2+}		Ni^{2+}		Cu^{2+}		Zn^{2+}		Cd^{2+}	
	NH_3	poly-amine	NH_3	poly-amine	NH_3	poly-amine	NH_3	poly-amine	NH_3	poly-amine
2	3·5	5·9	4·8	7·6	7·9	10·7	4·4	6·0	4·9	5·4
3	4·4	8·5	6·5	10·7	10·9	16·0	6·7	8·8	6·3	8·4
4	5·1	11·0	7·8	14·1	13·1	20·5	8·7	12·0	7·3	10·8
5	5·1	15·1	8·5	17·6	12·6	24·2		15·4	7·0	14·0
6	4·5	15·7	8·9	19·3		22·4		16·2	5·8	16·1
4†	5·1	12·8	7·8	14·8	13·1	18·7	8·7	14·6	7·3	12·3

†Polyamine complex with VI.

these amines forms complexes all amino groups fit comfortably into some of the octahedral sites with the formation of a series of five-membered chelate rings (e.g. V). Table 8 shows formation constants for complexes of these amines compared with the appropriate overall constants for co-ordination of the same number of nitrogen atoms as ammonia. The table also includes data for the 6:co-ordinate branched polyamine tetra(2-amino-ethyl)ethylenediamine (VII) and the branched 4:co-ordinate amine triaminotriethylamine (VI).

CH_2—CH_2
CH_2 NH NH_2
M
CH_2 NH NH_2
CH_2—CH_2

V

$CH_2CH_2NH_2$
CH_2–N–$CH_2CH_2NH_2$
CH_2–N–$CH_2CH_2NH_2$
$CH_2CH_2NH_2$

VI

$CH_2CH_2NH_2$
N—$CH_2CH_2NH_2$
$CH_2CH_2NH_2$

VII

While comparison of the formation constants shows how considerable stabilization is brought about, particularly by the amines with four, five or six nitrogen atoms, the data also reveal a number of interesting stereochemical results of using multidentate ligands of this type. Thus, although the overall constants for the addition of five or six ammonia molecules show that there is no large change in stability after the addition of the first four, the formation constants continue to rise with the 5- and 6-dentate amines; this is probably the best evidence that in complexes with these amines, all the amino groups are in fact co-ordinated. An exception occurs in the case of the Cu^{2+} ion where the lower value of the constant for the 6-dentate amine compared with the 5-dentate suggests that only five amino groups can be co-ordinated. This conclusion agrees well with the general features of copper(II) stereochemistry in the solid state, which were discussed in the previous chapter.

Comparison of the data for the two tetramines shows that for Co^{2+}, Ni^{2+}, Zn^{2+}, and Cd^{2+} the unbranched amine (V) forms less stable complexes than the branched amine (VI), but for Cu^{2+}, the complexes of the unbranched amine are more stable. This is attributed to the requirement that in a copper(II) complex the four most strongly held ligand atoms should be coplanar, which is not possible with the branched amine. A similar difference in behaviour of copper(II) from other metals is observed in the complexes of the corresponding quadridentate amino acids, the copper(II) complex of the unbranched acid (VIII) being more stable than that of the branched acid (IX).

$$\begin{array}{l} CH_2COOH \\ | \\ CH_2—NH \\ | \\ CH_2—NH \\ | \\ CH_2COOH \end{array} \qquad \begin{array}{l} CH_2—N(CH_2.COOH)_2 \\ | \\ CH_2—NH_2 \end{array}$$

VIII IX

Formation constant data are shown in Table 9, together with values of log β_2 for glycine, to show the stabilizing effect of increasing the number of chelate rings, whatever the shape of the ligand.

TABLE 9. FORMATION CONSTANTS, log k_1, OF COMPLEXES OF ETHYLENEDIAMINEDIACETIC ACIDS COMPARED WITH log β_2 OF GLYCINE COMPLEXES

Acid	Co^{2+}	Ni^{2+}	Cu^{2+}	Zn^{2+}	Cd^{2+}
VIII	11·2	13·5	16·2	11·1	8·8
IX	11·8	13·7	15·9	11·9	10·6
Glycine	8·4	11·0	15·1	9·3	8·8

Introduction of carboxylic acid groups into the molecule makes it possible to obtain stable complexes of metals which are not usually regarded as good complex formers. The replacement of nitrogen atoms in the amines by oxygen in carboxyl groups particularly favours complex formation by ions of inert-gas structure so that with these ligands stable complexes can be obtained in aqueous solution even with alkaline earth elements. The general reaction of amines with chloracetic acid has been utilized to produce a great variety of amino acids containing terminal

TABLE 10. FORMATION CONSTANTS, log k_1, OF COMPLEXES WITH SOME POLY-AMINO ACIDS

Acid	Mn^{2+}	Fe^{2+}	Co^{2+}	Ni^{2+}	Cu^{2+}	Zn^{2+}	Cd^{2+}	Mg^{2+}	Ca^{2+}	Sr^{2+}	Ba^{2+}
H_2NA	3·4	4·3	4·6	6·1	8·3	5·2	4·7	3·4	1·4	0·9	0·8
CH_3NA_2	5·4	6·6	7·6	8·7	11·1	9·6	6·8	3·4	3·8	2·8	2·6
NA_3	8·6	8·8	10·4	11·5	13·0	10·6	9·8	6·5	7·6	4·9	5·8
$N—NA_2$	7·7	9·8	11·8	13·7	15·9	11·9	10·6	4·5	4·6	3·5	3·2
$A_2N—NA_2$	13·8	14·3	16·2	18·0	18·5	16·4	16·4	8·6	10·5	8·5	7·8
$AN(NA_2)_2$ (branched: AN bonded to two NA₂ groups)	15·6	16·0	19·3	20·1	21·5	18·4	18·9		10·7	9·7	8·6

groups $—NCH_2CO_2H$, most of which form complexes with alkaline earth metals approaching in stability the complexes of transition metals. The best known of these amino acids is ethylenediaminetetraacetic acid, which can wrap round a cation so as to occupy all six octahedral sites (X), and has received considerable use as an analytical reagent. Formation constants of complexes of this and some other similar acids are given in Table 10, in which the formulae of the acids are represented symbolically: the symbol A stands for a $—CH_2CO_2H$ group and a heavy line joining two nitrogen atoms, **N—N**, represents a $—N.CH_2.CH_2.N—$ group, so that ethylenediaminetetraacetic acid is represented as A_2**N—N**A_2 and glycine as H_2NA.

X: $(HOOCCH_2)_2N—CH_2—CH_2—N(CH_2COOH)_2$

XI: $(HOOCCH_2)_2N—CH_2—CH_2—CH_2—N(CH_2COOH)_2$

XII: $(HOOCCH_2CH_2)_2N—CH_2—CH_2—N(CH_2CH_2COOH)_2$

The influence of varying ring size in these complexes is shown by the diaminetetracid compounds in which an extra CH_2 group is placed in either the central diamine ring (XI) or in the amino-acid rings (XII). Formation constant data for these ligands are given in Table 11.

TABLE 11. FORMATION CONSTANTS, log *k*, OF COMPLEXES WITH 5- AND 6-MEMBERED CHELATE RINGS

Acid	Mn^{2+}	Fe^{2+}	Co^{2+}	Ni^{2+}	Cu^{2+}	Zn^{2+}	Cd^{2+}	Mg^{2+}	Ca^{2+}	Sr^{2+}	Ba^{2+}
X	13·8	14·3	16·2	18·0	18·5	16·4	16·4	8·6	10·5	8·5	7·8
XI	15·6	16·5	19·0	20·2	21·1	18·4	13·4	6·0	7·1	5·2	4·2
XII	4·7	6·2	7·6	9·7	15·4	7·8	6·0	1·8			

Increasing the size of the amino-acid rings clearly brings about a substantial lowering of stability of all the complexes except that of copper(II); this distinction of copper(II) suggests that four donor atoms lie at the corners of a square in this case and that the problem of attaching two more donor atoms at the ends of long chains does not arise. It is interesting to observe that whereas increasing the central diamine ring to six-membered stabilizes complexes with transition metals, it destabilizes those with alkaline earth metals.

Enthalpy and Entropy of Chelation

The chelate effect can be explained qualitatively by comparing the first step in the dissociation of chelate and open chain type complexes:

$$M\begin{matrix}\diagup NH_3 \\ \diagdown NH_3\end{matrix} + OH_2 \rightleftharpoons M\begin{matrix}\diagup OH_2 \\ \diagdown NH_3\end{matrix} + NH_3$$

$$M\begin{matrix}\diagup NH_2-CH_2 \\ \diagdown NH_2-CH_2\end{matrix} + OH_2 \rightleftharpoons M\begin{matrix}\diagup OH_2 \qquad\qquad NH_2 \\ \diagdown NH_2-CH_2-CH_2\end{matrix}$$

In the above comparison of ammonia and ethylenediamine complexes, an ammonia molecule, once displaced, passes into the bulk of the solution and must compete for re-entry with the far more numerous water molecules; but when one end of an ethylenediamine molecule is displaced the amino-group is retained in the immediate neighbourhood of the metal atom and is consequently in a favourable position to compete with solvent molecules.

Quantitatively, the chelate effect can be seen to be an entropy effect, attributable to the change in the number of degrees of freedom of the system when a chelate ring is formed:

$$\underset{\text{two species}}{[M(OH_2)_2]+en} \rightleftharpoons \underset{\text{three species}}{[M(en)]+2H_2O}$$

When discussing the thermodynamic properties of equilibria of this type, it is usual to make the approximation that the enthalpy ΔH of the reaction is associated with the change in the metal–ligand bond energies. We should, therefore, expect that the enthalpy change when a complex is formed by a multidentate ligand should be similar to that observed for co-ordination of a corresponding number of monodentate ligands. Table 12 gives the observed values of ΔH for the co-ordination of multidentate polyamines compared with the cumulative enthalpies for the co-ordination of an equivalent number of ammonia molecules. The polyamines are the same as those for which formation constants are given in Table 8.

TABLE 12. ENTHALPIES OF FORMATION OF POLYAMINE COMPLEXES ΔH_1 COMPARED WITH ΔH_{β_n} FOR AMMONIA COMPLEXES (kcal/mole)

No. of N atoms co-ord.	Ni^{2+}		Cu^{2+}		Zn^{2+}	
	NH_3	poly-amine	NH_3	poly-amine	NH_3	poly-amine
1	−4·0	—	−5·9	—	−2·6	—
2	−7·6	−8·9	−11·5	−12·8	−5·7	−5·0
3	−12·1	−11·8	−17·5	−19·0	−9·6	−6·4
4	−15·4	−14·0	−20·0	−21·5	−11·8	−8·9

Comparison of Table 8 and Table 12 shows that whereas the enthalpy of formation of polyamine complexes is very similar to the cumulative enthalpy of formation of corresponding ammonia complexes, the formation constants, i.e. the free energies of formation, are much greater with the multidentate ligands, thus showing conclusively that the increased stability of these complexes is attributable almost wholly to the entropy term. From a study of all available data, it appears that the entropy contribution to stabilization is of the order of 3–6 entropy units per chelate ring formed at room temperature, when the ligand is a neutral molecule and 10–15 entropy units per chelate ring when the ligand is an anion.

Unsaturated Chelate Rings

Chelation by multidentate ligands of the polyamine and amino-acid types involves no fundamental change in the nature of the ligand. There is, however, a group of ligands which undergoes structural changes when forming a chelate ring. The simplest of these is acetylacetone. In the pure state this exists as a mixture of the keto- (XIII) and enol (XIV) forms; the enol form behaves as an acid and loses a proton forming an anion (XV) which behaves as a bidentate ligand.

$$CH_3-C(=O)-CH_2-C(=O)-CH_3 \qquad CH_3-C(=O)-CH=C(-OH)-CH_3 \qquad CH_3-C(=O)-CH=C(-O^-)-CH_3$$

XIII XIV XV

When the enolate anion forms a chelate ring, however, an important change in the electronic structure of the ligand occurs whereby the two oxygen atoms become equivalent. This change can be observed by infrared studies: the absorption band in the 1650–1750 cm^{-1} region, which is characteristic of the conjugated carbonyl group, $>C=O$, is absent from the infrared spectra of the complexes and instead new, very strong bands appear at about 1520 and 1590 cm^{-1}, which are characteristic of the new unsaturated system (XVI). There is one exception—the mercury(II) compound $(C_5H_7O_2)_2Hg$, in which the insistence of the mercury atom upon forming collinear bonds prevents the formation of chelate rings, still shows an absorption above 1600 cm^{-1}, characteristic of the $>C=O$ group (XVII).

The formation of the new conjugated system within the chelate ring evidently introduces considerable additional stabilization as the succes-

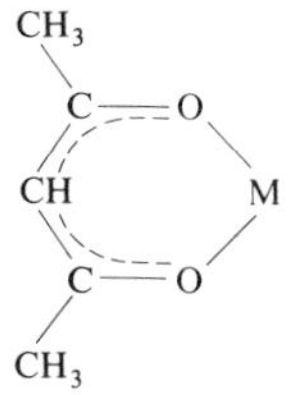

XVI 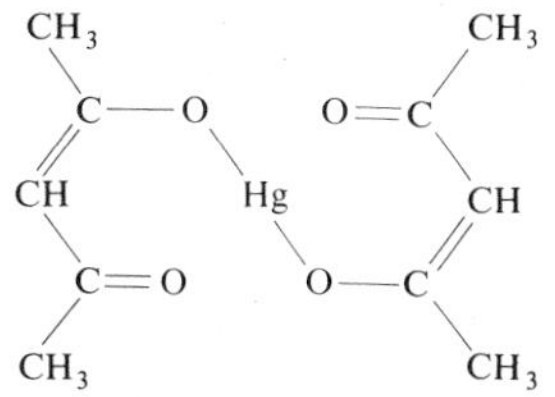 XVII

sive enthalpies of formation increase. With most ligands it has been found that successive enthalpies of formation are about equal, as shown for the ammonia complexes in Table 12. For acetylacetone complexes, however, there is an increase of 2–3 kcal/mole for each chelate ring formed and it seems reasonable to attribute this to the additional stabilization due to forming the new conjugated system. Some enthalpy data for acetylacetone complexes are shown in Table 13.

TABLE 13. SUCCESSIVE ENTHALPIES OF FORMATION $-\Delta H$ (kcal/mole) OF ACETYLACETONATO COMPLEXES

	Mn^{2+}	Co^{2+}	Ni^{2+}	Cu^{2+}	Zn^{2+}	Cd^{2+}	Be^{2+}	Mg^{2+}
ΔH_1	2·5	1·2	4·0	4·7	1·9	1·4	2·0	1·8
ΔH_2	4·7	5·0	6·3	6·6			6·9	4·3

When the number of acetylacetonate ions co-ordinated is the same as the oxidation state the complex formed is a neutral molecule and as the metal atom may then also be co-ordinately saturated, there results a series of very stable neutral complexes, soluble in organic solvents. The same type of neutral complexes can be formed by salicylaldehyde and *o*-hydroxy-aryl ketones but in these cases, infrared spectra of the complexes differ but slightly from those of the free ligand and the oxygen atoms cannot be considered equivalent. These ligands produce less stable complexes than acetylacetone; no enthalpy data are available but some first formation constants are given in Table 14, which also includes data for complexes formed by 8:hydroxyquinoline. Because of the sparing solubility of the organic compounds in water, data refer to solutions in

TABLE 14. FIRST FORMATION CONSTANTS, $\log k_1$, IN 50% DIOXANE

Ligand	Co^{2+}	Ni^{2+}	Cu^{2+}	Zn^{2+}	Cd^{2+}	Mg^{2+}
Acetylacetone	6·3	6·9	9·5	6·7	5·5	5·0
Salicylaldehyde	4·7	5·2	7·4	4·5	4·6	3·7
8:Hydroxyquinoline	10·6	11·4	13·5	10·0	9·4	6·4

50% aqueous dioxane, in which formation constants (log k) are commonly about one and a half times as great as in aqueous solutions.

CHANGE OF CO-ORDINATION NUMBER

The formation of complexes in aqueous solution does not normally involve any change in the co-ordination number of the metal atom. Formation constants and enthalpies of formation refer to replacement of co-ordinated water molecules by ligands. However, in non-donor solvents it is possible to observe co-ordination processes which involve changes in co-ordination number.

A familiar example of change of co-ordination number is provided by the reaction of cobalt(II) halides with bases. Compounds of the type CoX_2B_2 dissolve in non-donor solvents such as chloroform or benzene to give blue solutions, which from their colour contain tetrahedral molecules. On addition of excess free base the blue colour is destroyed and the pink, octahedral compounds CoX_2B_4 are formed. The process can be represented:

$$\underset{\text{3 species}}{CoX_2B_2 + 2B} \rightleftharpoons \underset{\text{1 species}}{CoX_2B_4}$$

During this process the number of species in solution is decreased, so that the entropy change can be expected to be in the opposite sense from chelation. Thermodynamic data have been obtained for this system at 25°C in chloroform solution with pyridine as base, and are given in Table 15.

TABLE 15. THERMODYNAMIC DATA FOR THE REACTION $CoX_2py_2 + 2py \rightleftharpoons CoX_2py_4$

X	Cl	Br	I	NCS	NCO
log k	1·08	0·94	0·36	4·81	1·33
$-\Delta G$ (kcal/mole)	1·48	1·28	0·49	6·60	1·83
$-\Delta H$ (kcal/mole)	15·2	15·6	16·6	16·6	13·7
$-\Delta S$ (e.u.)	46·8	48·8	54·9	34·1	40·5

Data from: King, H. C. A., Koros, E. and Nelson, S. M., *J. Chem. Soc.* (1963), 5449.

The value of about −15 for ΔH suggests a value of about −7·5 kcal/mole for each metal–nitrogen bond formed. Closely similar values have been observed for both ΔH and ΔS in the addition of two molecules of heterocyclic base to the square-planar nickel compound diacetyl-bis(benzoylhydrazone)nickel(II), Table 16.

TABLE 16. THERMODYNAMIC DATA FOR THE REACTION $Ni(DBH)_2 + 2\,base \rightleftharpoons Ni(DBH)_2base_2$

Base	Pyridine	4-mepy	2-mepy
log *k*	3·75	4·40	0·47
$-\Delta G$ (kcal/mole)	5·15	6·03	0·65
$-\Delta H$ (kcal/mole)	14·95	15·65	12·83
$-\Delta S$ (e.u.)	32·9	32·3	40·9

Data from: Sacconi, L., Lombardo, G. and Paoletti, P., *J. Inorg. Nucl. Chem.* (1958), **8**, 217.

Another reaction of this type which has been studied is the addition of heterocyclic bases to the square planar complexes of copper(II) with β-diketones to form 5:co-ordinate adducts:

$$CuA_2 + base \rightleftharpoons CuA_2base$$

For the system bis(acetylacetonato)copper(II)/pyridine in benzene solution at 25°C, a value of $-6{\cdot}0$ kcal/mole has been obtained for ΔH and this, combined with the formation constant, log k, of 0·87, gives a value of ΔS of -16 e.u. Values of ΔH varying between about 2 and 10 kcal/mole were obtained for other bases.†

FURTHER READING

BASOLO, F. and PEARSON, R. G., *Mechanisms of Inorganic Reactions—A Study of Metal Complexes in Solution*, John Wiley, New York (1958).

Chemical Society, *Kinetics and Mechanisms of Inorganic Reactions in Solution*, London (1957).

Chemical Society, *Stability Constants of Metal-ion Complexes*, 2nd ed., London (1964).

SCHWARTZENBACH, G., *Complexometric Titrations*, Interscience, New York (1957).

BJERRUM, J., On the tendency of the metal ions toward complex formation, *Chem. Rev.* **46**, 381 (1950).

BURKIN, A. R., Stabilities of complex compounds, *Quart. Rev.* **5**, 1 (1951).

CHATT, J., AHRLAND, S. and DAVIES, N. R., Relative affinities of ligand atoms for acceptor molecules and ions, *Quart. Rev.* **12**, 265 (1958).

GARVAN, F. L., Metal chelates of ethylenediaminetetraacetic acid and related substances, *Chelating Agents and Metal Chelates*, Eds. Mellor, D. P. and Dwyer, F. P., Academic Press, New York (1964).

GOODWIN, H. A., Design and stereochemistry of multidentate chelating agents, *Chelating Agents and Metal Chelates*, Eds. Mellor, D. P. and Dwyer, F. P., Academic Press, New York (1964).

ROSSOTTI, F. J. C., The thermodynamics of metal-ion complex formation in solution, *Modern Coordination Chemistry*, Eds. Lewis, J. and Wilkins, R. G., Interscience, New York (1960).

STRANKS, D. R., The reaction rates of transition metal complexes, *Modern Coordination Chemistry*, Eds. Lewis, J. and Wilkins, R. G., Interscience, New York (1960).

WILKINS, R. G., Kinetics and mechanisms of replacement reactions of coordination compounds, *Quart. Rev.* **16**, 316 (1962).

†(Data: May, W. R. and Jones, M. M., *J. Inorg. Nucl. Chem.* (1963), **25**, 507.) These values of ΔH and ΔS are about half those for the two previous systems, as might be expected for the addition of only one ligand.

CHAPTER V

THE STABILIZATION OF OXIDATION STATES

THE effect of complex formation in stabilizing certain valency states of metals is well known; familiar examples are the trivalent states of cobalt and gold. The oxidizing power of the hydrated cobalt(III) ion is so great that aqueous solutions of cobalt(III) salts, such as the sulphate or perchlorate, decompose spontaneously with the evolution of oxygen; conversely, the complex cobalt(II) cyanide ion reduces water with the evolution of hydrogen. Gold(III) provides a more extreme example, as this oxidation state of gold is known only in complex compounds nearly all of which have the square-planar configuration characteristic of low-spin d^8-ions.

When a metal can be obtained in aqueous solution in two different oxidation states, it is possible to measure the extent of valency stabilization brought about by complex formation; but in many instances this is not possible, and the stabilization of a particular oxidation state can then be recognized only by the isolation of characteristic compounds. It is thus necessary to distinguish between stabilization in a thermodynamic sense and stabilization indicated by the isolation of characteristic compounds, which may only be stable in inert atmospheres, or may owe their stability to lattice effects.

STANDARD REDUCTION POTENTIALS

The criterion by which the stability of one valency state with respect to another must be measured is the standard reduction potential of the system. The reduction potentials of such a system in the "free" (hydrated) and complexed forms are related to one another and to the stability constants of the complexes involved; this can readily be seen if the free energy changes ($\Delta G°$) for each successive step in the process of reduction of a complexed ion are considered:

$$M^{m+}_{aq} + n\bar{e} = M^{(m-n)+}_{aq} \qquad \Delta G° = -nFE°_{aq} \qquad (1)$$

$$ML^{m+}_{x} = M^{m+}_{aq} + xL \qquad +RT.\ln K_m \qquad (2)$$

$$M^{(m-n)+}_{aq} + yL = ML^{(m-n)+}_{y} \qquad -RT.\ln K_{m-n} \qquad (3)$$

$$ML^{m+}_{x} + n\bar{e} = ML^{(m-n)+}_{y} + (x-y)L \qquad -nFE°_{cx} \qquad (4)$$

Equation (1) represents the reduction of the "free" (hydrated) ion, M^{m+} to $M^{(m-n)+}$ and E°_{aq} is the standard reduction potential for this system; eqn. (4) represents the corresponding reduction of the complexed ion ML_x^{m+} for which the standard reduction potential is E°_{cx}; eqns. (2) and (3) represent the formation of the complex ions from the "free" ions and x- or y-molecules of the ligand L for which the stability constants are K_m and K_{m-n}, defined as:

$$K_m = \frac{[ML_x^{m+}]}{[M_{aq}^{m+}][L]^x} \qquad K_{m-n} = \frac{[ML_y^{(m-n)+}]}{[M_{aq}^{(m-n)+}][L]^y}$$

where the square brackets denote activities.

Now, since the free energy change must be the same by the direct and indirect routes, we have:

$$E^\circ_{cx} = E^\circ_{aq} - \frac{RT}{nF} \ln \frac{K_m}{K_{m-n}}$$

and consequently $E^\circ_{cx} < E^\circ_{aq}$ if $K_{m-n} < K_m$.

It is thus apparent that the stabilization of a valency state by complex formation depends upon the formation of thermodynamically more stable complexes in that valency state. The factors which affect the stability constants of complex salts have been discussed in the previous chapter; these factors are numerous, but there are two which are dominant:

(a) the valency (charge) of the complexed cation; and

(b) the polarizability (electronegativity) of the ligand L.

It follows that, in general, $K_{m-n} < K_m$ because of the first of these factors and that the ratio K_m/K_{m-n} is likely to increase with increasing polarizability (decreasing electronegativity) of the ligand, because of the second.

The general conclusion of this argument is that complex formation will stabilize higher valency states relative to lower and that the extent of the stabilization (i.e. $E^\circ_{aq} - E^\circ_{cx}$) will increase with increasing polarizability of the ligands. This general conclusion applies to all systems, irrespective of the electronic structures of the particular species involved, but it must be realized that in a few cases, where the other factors affecting the stability constants of one or more of the complex ions concerned become abnormally large, discrepancies may occur.

The simplest systems for which reduction potential data are available are those in which a metal electrode is in contact with a solution of an ion of the metal in aquated or complexed forms. Stabilization of the oxidation state of the metal represented by the ion relative to the oxidation state 0 is then indicated by a more positive value of the reduction potential of the system

$$M^{n+} + ne \rightleftharpoons M$$

Data for some complex halides are given in Table 1 and for complex cyanides in Table 2.

TABLE 1. REDUCTION POTENTIALS OF AQUATED IONS AND HALIDE COMPLEXES (volts)

Metal and ion	Formula of complex	E° aquated	E° X = Cl	E° X = Br
Pd, Pd^{2+}	PdX_4^{2-}	+0·99	+0·62	+0·6
Pt, Pt^{2+}	PtX_4^{2-}	+1·2	+0·73	+0·58
Au, Au^{3+}	AuX_4^-	+1·50	+1·00	+0·86
Au, Au^+	AuX_2^-	+1·68	+1·13	+0·96
Rh, Rh^{3+}	RhX_6^{3-}	+0·8	+0·44	

TABLE 2. REDUCTION POTENTIALS OF AQUATED IONS AND CYANIDE COMPLEXES (volts)

Metal and ion	Formula of Complex	E° aquated	E° complexed
Ni, Ni^{2+}	$Ni(CN)_4^{2-}$	−0·25	−0·91
Cu, Cu^+	$Cu(CN)_2^-$	+0·52	−0·43
Ag, Ag^+	$Ag(CN)_2^-$	+0·80	−0·29
Au, Au^+	$Au(CN)_2^-$	+1·13	−0·61
Zn, Zn^{2+}	$Zn(CN)_4^{2-}$	−0·76	−1·32
Cd, Cd^{2+}	$Cd(CN)_4^{2-}$	−0·40	−0·90
Hg, Hg^{2+}	$Hg(CN)_4^{2-}$	+0·85	−0·37

From the data in these tables it is apparent that the oxidation states +1, +2 or +3 are stabilized relative to the oxidation state 0 in all cases. Formation of halide complexes leads to stabilization by about 0·5 V, of cyanide complexes by a rather larger amount. A familiar practical result of the stabilization brought about by cyanide complex formation is the solubility of metallic silver and gold in aqueous cyanide solutions.

When a metal forms complexes in more than one oxidation state with the same ligand, the difference between the reduction potentials of the systems

$$M_{aq}^{m+} + n\bar{e} \rightleftharpoons M_{aq}^{(m-n)+};\ E^\circ_{aq}$$

$$M_{cx}^{m+} + n\bar{e} \rightleftharpoons M_{cx}^{(m-n)+};\ E^\circ_{cx}$$

indicates the extent to which complex formation stabilizes one oxidation state relative to another. Table 3 gives data for a range of complex cyanide systems and Table 4 gives data for some complex halide and thiocyanate systems, for which however, the reduction potentials of corresponding aquated systems are often unknown.

TABLE 3. REDUCTION POTENTIALS OF AQUATED SYSTEMS AND CORRESPONDING CYANIDE COMPLEXES (volts)

Ions	E°_{aq}	Complex ions	E°_{cx}
Cr^{3+}, Cr^{2+}	-0.41	$Cr(CN)_6^{3-}$, $Cr(CN)_6^{4-}$	-1.28
Mn^{3+}, Mn^{2+}	$+0.77$	$Mn(CN)_6^{3-}$, $Mn(CN)_6^{4-}$	-0.24
Fe^{3+}, Fe^{2+}	$+0.77$	$Fe(CN)_6^{3-}$, $Fe(CN)_6^{4-}$	$+0.36$
Co^{3+}, Co^{2+}	$+1.84$	$Co(CN)_6^{3-}$, $Co(CN)_5^{3-}$	-0.80

TABLE 4. REDUCTION POTENTIALS OF COMPLEX HALIDE AND THIOCYANATE SYSTEMS (volts)

Ions	E°_{aq}	Complex ions	E°_{cx}			
			X = Cl	X = Br	X = I	X = NCS
Rh^{4+}, Rh^{3+}	$+1.44$	RhX_6^{2-}, RhX_6^{3-}	$+1.2$			
Ir^{4+}, Ir^{3+}		IrX_6^{2-}, IrX_6^{3-}	$+1.03$	$+0.99$	$+0.49$	
Pd^{4+}, Pd^{2+}		PdX_6^{2-}, PdX_4^{2-}	$+1.29$	$+0.99$	$+0.48$	
Pt^{4+}, Pt^{2+}		PtX_6^{2-}, PtX_4^{2-}	$+0.75$	$+0.59$	$+0.39$	$+0.47$
Au^{3+}, Au^{+}	$+1.29$	AuX_4^{-}, AuX_2^{-}	$+0.94$	$+0.81$		$+0.65$

The stabilization of the upper oxidation state brought about by cyanide co-ordination varies considerably from metal to metal, amounting to 0·4 V in the Fe^{3+}–Fe^{2+} system and 2·6 V in the Co^{3+}–Co^{2+} system. Stabilization by halide co-ordination is usually less than that brought

TABLE 5. REDUCTION POTENTIALS OF COMPLEX IONS AND SPARINGLY SOLUBLE COMPOUNDS OF COPPER(I) AND SILVER(I) (volts)

Complex	$E^{\circ}(Cu^{+}-Cu)$	$E^{\circ}(Ag^{+}-Ag)$
M^{+}(aqueous)	$+0.52$	$+0.80$
$M(NH_3)_2^{+}$	-0.12	$+0.37$
MN_3	-0.03	$+0.29$
MCl	$+0.14$	$+0.22$
MSCN	-0.27	$+0.09$
MBr	$+0.03$	$+0.07$
MI	-0.19	-0.15
$M(CN)_2^{-}$	-0.43	-0.29
M_2S	-0.93	-0.71

about by cyanide and the increasing stabilization with increasing polarizability of the halide is apparent from Table 4. A more extensive comparison of the stabilizing effect of different ligands is possible if we consider insoluble compounds as extensive co-ordinated systems; the data in Table 5 include sparingly soluble compounds and complex ions of Cu^+ and Ag^+ relative to the metal.

While the data in Tables 1–5 show the general effect of complex formation in stabilizing a higher oxidation state of a metal, as expected, there are special features of some systems which make it desirable to discuss these systems in more detail.

The Silver(II)–Silver(I) System

Silver(I) can be oxidized to silver(II) by the action of ozone in nitric acid solution but the aquated Ag^{2+} ion is so powerful an oxidizing agent that it decomposes water with the evolution of oxygen. Its reduction potential should be lowered by complex formation and as considerable lowering is required to effect stabilization, ligands of high polarizability are required. Unfortunately, such ligands are usually sensitive to oxidation and so cannot be used. Heterocyclic bases, however, have been found to provide sufficient stabilization, and the only extensive series of silver(II) compounds known are those in which the ion is co-ordinated to these bases. The following values have been given for the reduction potentials of the Ag^{2+}–Ag^+ system:

$$Ag^{2+} + \bar{e} \rightleftharpoons Ag^+ \qquad E^\circ = +1{\cdot}98 \text{ V}$$
$$2AgO_{(s)} + 2H^+ + 2\bar{e} \rightleftharpoons Ag_2O + H_2O \qquad E^\circ = +1{\cdot}40 \text{ V}$$
$$Ag(dipy)_2^{2+} + \bar{e} \rightleftharpoons Ag(dipy)_2^+ \qquad E^\circ = +0{\cdot}81 \text{ V}$$

The complex silver(II) salts, which can be readily made by oxidation of solutions of silver(I) salts and heterocyclic bases in water, resemble those of copper(II), with which they are often isomorphous. They are orange and paramagnetic, with one unpaired electron per silver atom.

The Cobalt(III)–Cobalt(II) System

This system provides one of the most remarkable examples of stabilization of a higher oxidation state by complex formation. The aquated cobalt(III) ion is so powerful an oxidizing agent that it decomposes water but co-ordination, particularly of amino groups or cyanide ions, stabilizes the cobalt(III) to the extent where ammoniacal or cyanide solutions of cobalt(II) are oxidized by exposure to air. The effect of co-ordination on the reduction potential of the system is shown in Table 6.

At one time the exceptional stability of these cobalt(III) complexes was attributed to the inert-gas configuration of the metal atom in the complex:

	3d					4s	4p		
	—	—	—	—	—	—	—	—	—
Co^{3+}	⇅	↓	↓	↓	↓				
CoX_6^{3+}	⇅	⇅	⇅	⇅	⇅	⇅	⇅	⇅	⇅
				X	X	X	X	X	X

TABLE 6. REDUCTION POTENTIALS OF THE COBALT(III)–COBALT(II) SYSTEM (volts)

Ions	$E°$
Co^{3+}, Co^{2+}	+1·84
$Co(NH_3)^{3+}$, $Co(NH_3)^{2+}$	+1·53
$Co(NH_3)_2^{3+}$, $Co(NH_3)_2^{2+}$	+1·22
$Co(NH_3)_3^{3+}$, $Co(NH_3)_3^{2+}$	+0·95
$Co(NH_3)_4^{3+}$, $Co(NH_3)_4^{2+}$	+0·63
$Co(NH_3)_5^{3+}$, $Co(NH_3)_5^{2+}$	+0·35
$Co(NH_3)_6^{3+}$, $Co(NH_3)_6^{2+}$	+0·10
Co en_3^{3+}, Co en_3^{2+}	−0·19
$Co(CN)_6^{3-}$, $Co(CN)_5^{3-}$	−0·80
$Co(EDTA)^-$, $Co(EDTA)^{2-}$	+0·68

but it has been found that not only the complexes but also the aquated ions have the low-spin configuration. The unusually great stabilization of cobalt(III) brought about by co-ordination must thus be attributed to unusually large formation constants of cobalt(III) complexes. Table 7 gives values of the overall constants for the formation of some cobalt(III) complexes and comparison with values of divalent ions (Tables 8, 10: Chapter IV) shows that the formation constants for these cobalt(III) complexes are quite exceptionally high.

TABLE 7. OVERALL FORMATION CONSTANTS (Log K) FOR COBALT(III) COMPLEXES

$Co(NH_3)_6^{3+}$	34
$Co(en)_3^{3+}$	49
$Co(EDTA)^-$	36
$Co(CN)_6^{3-}$	64

However, the range of ligands which form such stable complexes with cobalt(III) is very restricted and consequently the stabilization of cobalt(III) is quite specific. In addition to ammonia and aliphatic amines stable cobalt(III) complexes are also formed with many O-donors such as carboxylic acids and β-diketones and with cyanide. Although formation constant or reduction potential data are usually not available; the general behaviour of cobalt(II) and cobalt(III) complexes, particularly in solution, provide a reasonable guide to the extent to which particular ligands stabilize cobalt(III).

Aqueous solutions of cobalt(II) salts to which cyanide, ammonia or aliphatic amines have been added are oxidized rapidly on exposure to air. When aromatic amines, such as aniline, are used the oxidation appears to be less rapid and replacement of the amine by a heterocyclic base prevents this oxidation. Indeed, cobalt(III) complexes cannot be prepared with many molecules of pyridine co-ordinated to the metal. Replacement of pyridine by the bidentate bases bipyridyl or phenanthroline is accompanied by the usual increase in stability associated with chelation and tris-complexes of cobalt(III) can be isolated. These complexes, however, are very readily reduced to cobalt(II) complexes and are much less stable than the corresponding ethylenediamine complexes; they cannot, for example, be resolved into optical isomers.

Oxygen donors, such as carboxylic acids and β-diketones stabilize cobalt(III) but to a lesser extent than amines. Thus tris(glycinato)-cobalt(III) and tris(acetylacetonato)cobalt(III) are highly stable compounds, but the corresponding cobalt(II) compounds can also be readily obtained and are not particularly sensitive to oxidation. An interesting example of the effect of pyridine in stabilizing cobalt(II) is provided by the behaviour of bis(acetylacetonato)cobalt(II). This compound is usually obtained as the octahedral diaquo complex and solutions of this in ethanol are quite stable to air, but solutions of the anhydrous compound in benzene are rapidly oxidized on exposure; addition of pyridine to these solutions, which produces bis-pyridine-bis(acetylacetonato)cobalt(II), completely inhibits oxidation.

It is not clear what explanation can be offered for the remarkably different effects of ammonia and pyridine on the cobalt(II)–cobalt(III) system. It has been suggested that under suitable conditions co-ordinated pyridine can be involved in "back co-ordination" of electrons in the metal *d*-orbitals to vacant orbitals in the aromatic system; the effect of such back co-ordination would be to increase the nett positive charge on the metal atom, a situation most undesirable when the metal is in a comparatively high oxidation state. We might thus expect to find a general tendency for heterocyclic bases to stabilize lower oxidation states, particularly when the conditions for back co-ordination are satisfied in the higher oxidation states. Back co-ordination can be expected particularly from completely filled *d*-orbitals, that is, from d^{10}-ions, such as cobalt(III) and it is interesting to observe that other ions of high oxidation state with d^{10}-structures, notably Pd^{4+} and Pt^{4+}, also fail to form stable complexes with heterocyclic bases.

The Iron(II)–Iron(III) System

Oxidation-reduction relationships in the iron(II)–iron(III) system are complicated by the occurrence of complexes of both oxidation states in both high- and low-spin configurations. In the previous chapter it has been shown that the much greater spin-pairing energy of iron(III) compared with iron(II) leads to the stabilization of iron(II) relative to iron(III) in low-spin complexes except when the orbital separation produced by the ligands is very large. Complexes of bipyridyl and phenanthroline provide examples of this.

Although phenanthroline thus produces an unusual stabilization of the lower oxidation state, substitution in the phenanthroline produces variations in this stabilization of the sort which would usually be expected. Thus substitution by methyl groups which could be expected to increase the donor power of the phenanthroline and so to stabilize relatively the upper oxidation state, does just this; and substitution by nitro-groups provides the most extreme stabilization of the lower state (Table 8).

TABLE 8. REDUCTION POTENTIALS OF THE Fe^{3+}–Fe^{2+} SYSTEM IN LOW-SPIN COMPLEXES (volts)

Complexes	$E°$
$Fe(nitro\text{-}phen)_3^{3+}$, $Fe(nitro\text{-}phen)_3^{2+}$	+1·25
$Fe(phen)_3^{3+}$, $Fe(phen)_3^{2+}$	+1·12
$Fe(bipy)_3^{3+}$, $Fe(bipy)_3^{2+}$	+1·10
$Fe(4{:}7\text{-}Me_2\text{-}phen)_3^{3+}$, $Fe(4{:}7\text{-}Me_2\text{-}phen)_3^{2+}$	+0·88
$Fe(CN)_6^{3-}$, $Fe(CN)_6^{4-}$	+0·36

When co-ordination occurs without change of spin the usual result is the expected one of stabilization of the upper oxidation state. Table 9

TABLE 9. REDUCTION POTENTIALS OF THE Fe^{3+}–Fe^{2+} SYSTEM IN HIGH-SPIN COMPLEXES (volts)

Ligand, and number of ligands co-ordinated to metal atoms	$E°$
Aqueous solution	+0·77
8:Hydroxyquinoline anion–1	+0·55
8:Hydroxyquinoline anion–2	+0·37
8:Hydroxyquinoline anion–3	+0·07
Pyridine 2-carboxylate ion–2	+0·54
Glycinate ion–1	+0·40
Salicylate ion–1	+0·18
Salicylate ion–2	−0·23
EDTA anion–1	+0·12
Triethylenetetramine–1	−0·07
Hydroxyl ion–4	−0·73

shows typical examples; most of the values in the table have been calculated from formation constant data, as direct measurements of $E°$ have not been made.

Formation constant data are available for complexes of iron in both oxidation states with about thirty different ligands. Among these is a small group which, although not causing spin pairing, form more stable complexes with iron(II) than with iron(III), thus stabilizing the lower oxidation state. The ligands which behave in this way include histamine (I), histidine (II) and a number of compounds which are used medicinally as antihistamines including benadryl (III) and ephedrine (IV)

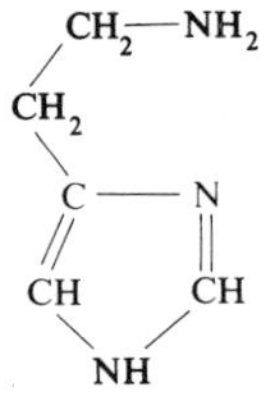

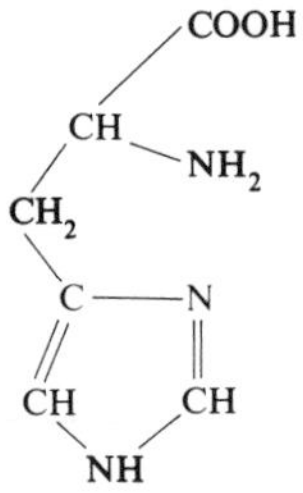

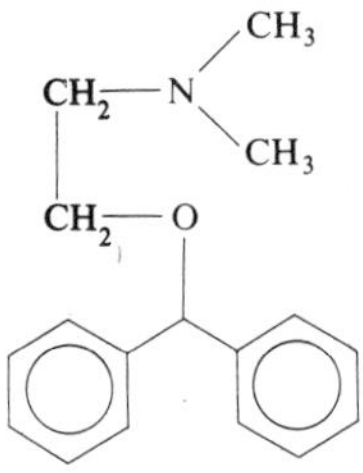

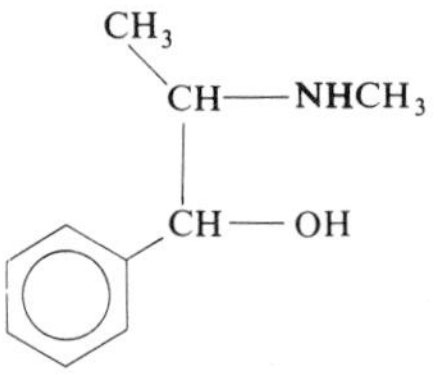

TABLE 10. FIRST FORMATION CONSTANTS OF COMPLEXES OF IRON(II) AND IRON(III) WITH HISTAMINE AND SOME RELATED COMPOUNDS

Ligand	$\log K_1(Fe^{2+})$	$\log K_1(Fe^{3+})$
Histamine	5·85	4·00
Histidine	5·80	3·72
Benadryl	5·85	4·05
Ephedrine	6·25	3·68
Bis(2-hydroxyethyl)glycine	4·31	3·00
Glycine	3·83	10·00

All these compounds are aliphatic amines; benadryl and ephedrine have no other groups in the molecule which seem likely to co-ordinate. The formation constants for the complexes with one molecule of ligand are all very similar (Table 10) and comparison with constants for co-ordination of one glycinate anion suggests that in the iron (III) complexes the ligands are monodentate; the stability of the iron(II) complexes is surprisingly high, higher than that of the monoglycinate complex, and there does not seem to be any ready explanation for this.

UNUSUALLY HIGH OXIDATION STATES

Most of the transition metals in the first long period form their most numerous compounds in oxidation states +2 and +3, and it has become customary to think of higher oxidation states as unusual. However, all the metals from titanium to iron are known in oxidation state +4 or higher. The most characteristic compounds of this type are the salts of the acidic oxides, for example, vanadates, chromates and permangates.

It is reasonable, though not usual, to regard the ions, such as VO_4^{3-} CrO_4^{2-} or MnO_4^-, as complex ions in which four O^{2-} ions as ligands are co-ordinated to a central V^{5+}, Cr^{6+} or Mn^{7+} ion. The essential criterion for stability in such complex ions is that the ligands should provide a means for dissipating the enormous concentration of charge on the metal atoms. When the ligands are simple this can be achieved only by the co-ordination of donor atoms of high electronegativity, such as oxygen or fluorine. Thus almost all compounds of transition metals in very high oxidation states are either simple or complex oxides or fluorides.

To a certain extent it is possible to replace oxygen or fluorine by other halogens, for example, the oxide-halides $VOCl_3$ and CrO_2Cl_2 and the complex ion CrO_3Cl^-, but this sort of replacement is limited by the tendency of the metal cation to oxidize the ligand. With transition metals of the second and third long periods, a wider range of halogen compounds can be obtained, such as $MoCl_5$, WCl_6 and WBr_6, since the metal ions are not such powerful oxidizing agents. A considerable variety of complex compounds is known with molybdenum and tungsten, for example, the complex sulphide ions MoS_4^{3-}, WS_4^{2-} and cyanide and thiocyanate complexes such as $[Mo^{V}O(NCS)_5]^{2-}$, $[Mo^{V}(CN)_8]^{3-}$, $[Mo^{IV}(CN)_8]^{4-}$ and corresponding tungsten compounds.

Although high oxidation states such as Cr^{VI} and Mn^{VII} are observed in oxide or fluoride complexes, these ligands do not so much provide stabilization of the oxidation state as protection: the complex ions CrO_4^{2-} and MnO_4^- are powerful oxidizing agents but the immediate environment of the metal atom is not oxidizable. High oxidation states of some of the later transition metals can be similarly obtained in fluoride complexes, for example, silver(III) in the AgF_4^- ion, cobalt(IV), nickel(IV) and palladium(IV) in the ions CoF_6^{2-}, NiF_6^{2-} and PdF_6^{2-} and platinum(VI) in the fluoride PtF_6.

Consideration of the factors which affect formation constants of complex compounds suggests that it should also be possible to stabilize such high oxidation states by co-ordination of ligands of low electronegativity and high polarizability, provided oxidation of the ligands can be avoided.

The principle of stabilization of higher valency states by ligands of low electronegativity is well illustrated by the complex compounds of Ni^{3+} and Ni^{4+}, in which the nickel atom is co-ordinated to phosphorus or arsenic atoms.

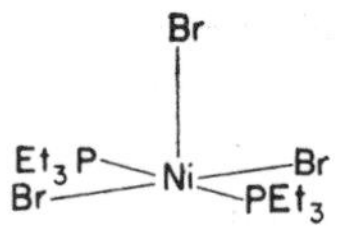

Br; Et_3P; Ni; Br; Br; PEt_3

V

$As(CH_3)_2$; $As(CH_3)_2$

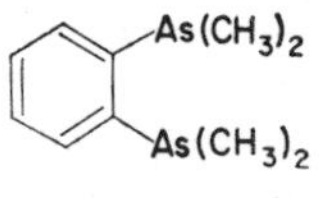

VI

The diamagnetic, square-planar complex bis-triethylphosphine nickel bromide, $[(Et_3P)_2NiBr_2]$, can be oxidized to the corresponding trivalent nickel derivative, $[(Et_3P)_2NiBr_3]$, paramagnetic and monomeric in benzene solution, for which a square-pyramidal structure, (V), has been proposed on the basis of dipole-moment measurements. The 4:co-ordinate nickel chloride derivative of the bidentate ligand *o*-phenylene-bis-dimethylarsine (VI), $[Ni(diarsine)_2]Cl_2$, can be similarly oxidized to the trivalent nickel derivative, which is a uni-univalent electrolyte in nitrobenzene and so regarded as a 6 :co-ordinated complex, $[Ni(diarsine)_2Cl_2]Cl$; the formation of 6:co-ordinated Ni^{3+} requires the promotion of one electron beyond the krypton shell, probably to the 5*s*-orbital, and consequently this compound is readily oxidized to the corresponding Ni^{4+} derivative, $[Ni(diarsine)_2Cl_2]Cl_2$. The Ni^{4+} ion also occurs in some sulphur co-ordinated complexes and in the fluoride K_2NiF_6; all are diamagnetic.

	3*d*					4*s*	4*p*			5*s*
	—	—	—	—	—	—	—	—	—	—
$[Ni(diarsine)_2]^{2+}$	⥮	⥮	⥮	⥮	⥮	⥮	⥮	⥮		
$[Ni(diarsine)_2Cl_2]^+$	⥮	⥮	⥮	⥮	⥮	⥮	⥮	⥮	⥮	↓
$[Ni(diarsine)_2Cl_2]^{2+}$	⥮	⥮	⥮	⥮	⥮	⥮	⥮	⥮	⥮	

The use of the ligand *o*-phenylene-bis-dimethylarsine has also made possible the stabilization of the tetravalent state of iron: with ferric chloride the doubly complex $[Fe(diarsine)_2Cl_2][FeCl_4]$ is obtained with the iron trivalent in both complex ions; this, when oxidized with nitric acid, gives the corresponding complex of tetravalent iron, $[Fe(diarsine)_2Cl_2][FeCl_4]_2$, in which the iron atom co-ordinated to four arsenic atoms is in the four valent state, as is confirmed by the paramagnetism of the compound which corresponds to the presence of two unpaired electrons on this iron atom.

UNUSUALLY LOW OXIDATION STATES

Isolation of compounds of transition metals in oxidation states lower than +2 can be achieved by reduction reactions in non-aqueous solvents.

Reduction of the complex nickel cyanide, $K_2[Ni(CN)_4]$, by metallic potassium in solution in liquid ammonia produces the compound $K_2Ni(CN)_3$, known as Belluci's salt. This compound is diamagnetic and must thus be polymerized since the monomeric compound would contain an odd number of electrons. X-ray analysis has established the bridged structure (VII), and since infrared analysis reveals only the normal C≡N stretching frequencies of the cyanide ion it is concluded that the bridging groups must be linked by three-centre bonds. Further reduction of the nickel cyanide complex under the same conditions gives the Ni° complex, $K_4[Ni(CN)_4]$. Corresponding compounds of palladium and cobalt in the zero-valent state are obtained in the same way.

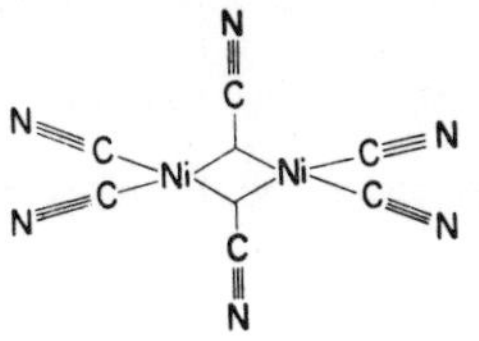

VII

$$(NC)_4\text{—Co—Co—}(CN)_4$$

VIII

The nickel and palladium compounds are diamagnetic and presumably have tetrahedral anions. The $[Ni(CN)_4]^{4-}$ ion would be isoelectronic with the nickel carbonyl molecule, $Ni(CO)_4$, the unusual stabilization of the low Ni° valency by cyanide co-ordination being attributed to the possibility of double bonding between the nickel and carbon atoms as in the carbonyl:

$$Ni \leftarrow C \equiv N\text{—} \longleftrightarrow Ni \rightleftarrows C = N\langle$$

The cobalt compound is very feebly paramagnetic and so probably dimeric; by analogy with the carbonyl, $Co_2(CO)_8$, an ion with Co—Co bonds is postulated (VIII).

Ammines of metals in low oxidation states have also been obtained by reduction with alkali metals. These compounds appear to be most stable when the ligand is a highly aromatic system such as bipyridyl or phenanthroline. Thus reduction of tris-bipyridylmolybdenum(III) chloride with lithium bipyridyl in tetrahydrofuran gives tris-bipyridyl molybdenum (0). Corresponding compounds $[Nb^{\circ}(bipy)_3]$ and $[W^{\circ}(bipy)_3]$ are obtained by similar reduction of the halides $NbCl_5$ or WCl_6. Reduction of tris-bipyridyl cobalt(II) perchlorate by sodium borohydride in ethanol gives the cobalt(I) complex $[Co^{I}(bipy)_3]ClO_4$. Although most of the low oxidation state compounds obtained in this way have bipyridyl, phenanthroline or similar ligands, these are not essential as reduction of hexammineosmium(III) bromide by potassium in liquid ammonia has led to the compounds $[Os^{I}(NH_3)_6]Br$ and $[Os^{\circ}(NH_3)_6]$.

The majority of low oxidation state compounds, however, are derivatives of carbonyls, π-complexes or phosphines and these are discussed in the following chapter.

FURTHER READING

Chemical Society, *Stability Constants of Metal-ion Complexes*, 2nd ed., London (1964).

LATIMER, W. M., *Oxidation States of the Elements and their Potentials in Aqueous Solution*, 2nd ed., Prentice-Hall, New York (1952).

CROW, D. R. and WESTWOOD, J. V., The study of complexed metal ions by polarographic methods, *Quart. Rev.* **19**, 57 (1965).

NYHOLM, R. S. and TOBE, M. L., The stabilization of oxidation states of the transition metals, *Advances Inorg. Chem., Radiochem.* **5**, 1 (1963).

PERRIN, D. D., Oxidation-reduction potentials of complex ions, *Rev. Pure App. Chem.* **9**, 257 (1959).

TAUBE, H., Mechanisms of redox reactions of simple chemistry, *Advances Inorg. Chem., Radiochem.* **1**, 1 (1959).

CHAPTER VI

CARBONYLS AND Π-COMPLEXES

THE discovery of nickel and iron carbonyls by Mond in 1890 and his use of the former in the nickel-refining process known by his name opened up a new field of chemistry, characterized by the formation of compounds by metals in the zero-valent state. The direct action of carbon monoxide under pressure on metals in a finely divided state gives carbonyls only with iron, cobalt, nickel, molybdenum, rhenium and ruthenium; carbonyls of other transition metals are obtained by the action of carbon monoxide on their compounds in organic solvents during their reaction with Grignard reagents or by the reaction between carbon monoxide and the *cyclo*pentadienyls at elevated temperatures.

In most known carbonyls the metal atom acquires the electronic structure of the next inert gas. Thus only the metals of even atomic number in groups VI–VIII form monomeric carbonyls, the stereochemistry of which is that expected for compounds with co-ordination numbers of six, five and four: the $M(CO)_6$ carbonyls of the group VI elements form octahedral molecules; those of iron, ruthenium and osmium have trigonal bipyramidal $M(CO)_5$ molecules and nickel carbonyl, $Ni(CO)_4$, is tetrahedral; corresponding carbonyls of palladium and platinum are not known.

	3*d*					4*s*	4*p*		
$Cr(CO)_6$	⇅	⇅	⇅	⇅	⇅	⇅	⇅	⇅	⇅
				CO	CO	CO	CO	CO	CO
$Fe(CO)_5$	⇅	⇅	⇅	⇅	⇅	⇅	⇅	⇅	⇅
					CO	CO	CO	CO	CO
$Ni(CO)_4$	⇅	⇅	⇅	⇅	⇅	⇅	⇅	⇅	⇅
						CO	CO	CO	CO

Electron diffraction studies of nickel carbonyl also showed that the Ni—C—O groups were linear, with unexpectedly short Ni—C bonds, the measured bond length of 1·82 Å being 0·37 Å shorter than that calculated for a Ni—C single bond; the C—O distance of 1·15 Å is intermediate between that of the C—O double and triple bonds. These results are interpreted as indicating considerable contribution to the structure from the double-bonded form (II), which is produced by "back co-ordination" of the non-bonding 3*d*-electrons on the nickel atom to the carbon monoxide molecules.

$$\underset{\text{I}}{Ni \leftarrow C \equiv N-} \longleftrightarrow \underset{\text{II}}{Ni \rightleftarrows C = O\!\!<}$$

The simplest carbonyls of the intervening elements of odd atomic number are dimeric, manganese and rhenium forming $Mn_2(CO)_{10}$ and $Re_2(CO)_{10}$ and cobalt $Co_2(CO)_8$ in accordance with the principle of completion of the inert-gas structure of the metal atom; the molecular complexities of the carbonyls of rhodium and iridium of the type $[M(CO)_4]_n$ are not known, but are probably similar.

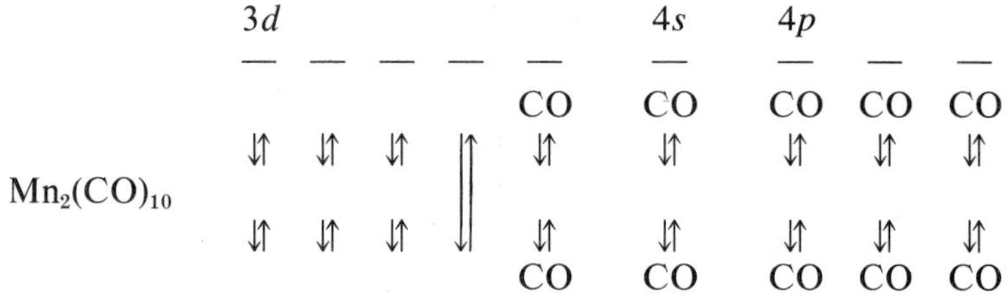

	3*d*					4*s*	4*p*		
					CO	CO	CO	CO	CO
	⥮	⥮	⥮	↿	⥮	⥮	⥮	⥮	⥮
$Mn_2(CO)_{10}$				|					
	⥮	⥮	⥮	⇃	⥮	⥮	⥮	⥮	⥮
					CO	CO	CO	CO	CO

The dimeric carbonyls of manganese and rhenium have been shown to have the two halves of the molecule linked only by direct metal–metal bonds (III), as indicated in the electronic diagram above. The corresponding cobalt compound, however, has the halves linked by a metal–metal bond and two bridging ketonic carbonyl groups (IV).

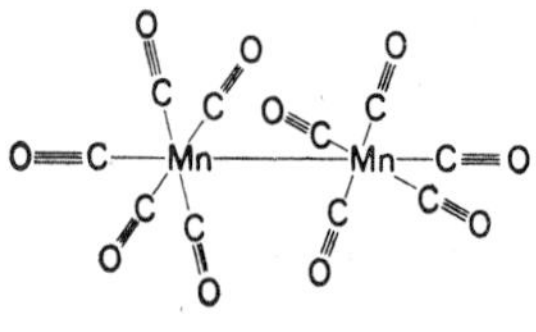

III

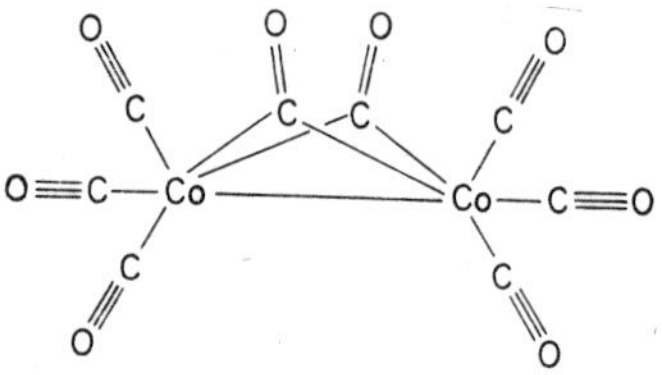

IV

$Ni(CO)_4$ (b.p. 43°C), $Fe(CO)_5$ (b.p. 103°C), $Ru(CO)_5$, $Os(CO)_5$ and $Co_2(CO)_8$ are liquids, the last three decomposing below 100°C to give polymeric solid carbonyls; the other carbonyls are all solids, those of the group VI metals subliming at temperatures of 100–200°C without decomposition, though all carbonyls are eventually decomposed to the metals and carbon monoxide by heat, the nickel compound particularly readily; all are immiscible with water but more or less soluble in organic solvents; the readily-volatile carbonyls, such as the nickel and iron compounds, are very poisonous.

On exposure to light or heat iron carbonyl loses carbon monoxide with the formation of a yellow, solid, dimeric carbonyl, $Fe_2(CO)_9$, which disproportionates above 60°C giving $Fe(CO)_5$ and a dark green solid carbonyl $Fe_3(CO)_{12}$, the molecular weight of which was determined by the depression of freezing point of the pentacarbonyl.

$$6Fe(CO)_5 - 3CO \xrightarrow{\text{light}} 3Fe_2(CO)_9 \xrightarrow[60°C]{} Fe_3(CO)_{12} + 3Fe(CO)_5$$

All these carbonyls are diamagnetic, so that the iron atom probably has the inert-gas structure of krypton in each case. The structure of the ennea-carbonyl, $Fe_2(CO)_9$, has been determined by X-ray analysis: the iron atoms are linked by three covalent "ketonic" $>C=O$ bridges and as the Fe—Fe distance of 2·46 Å is that expected for the Fe—Fe single

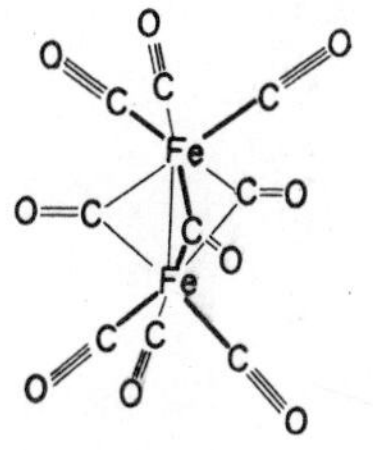

V

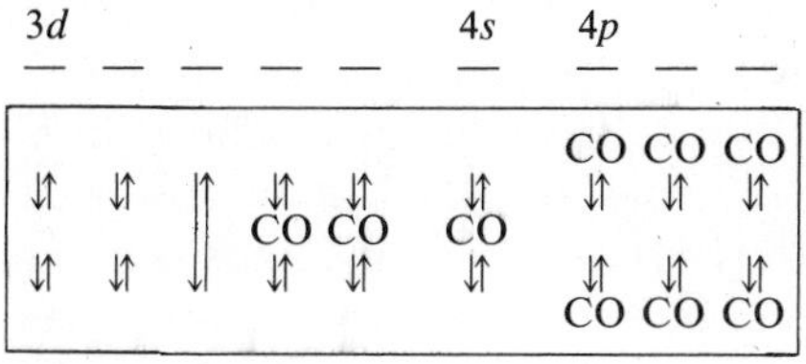

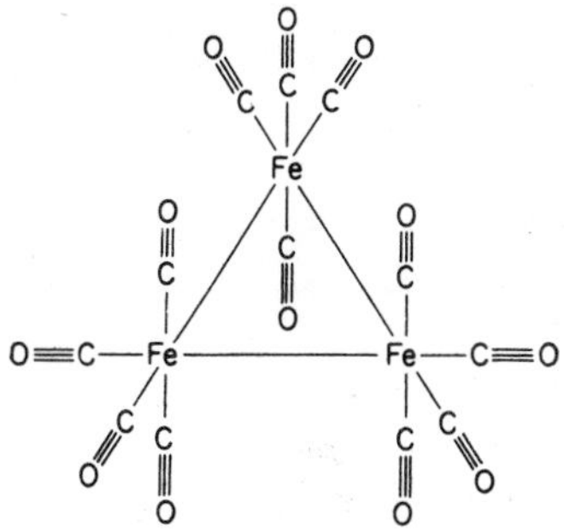

VI

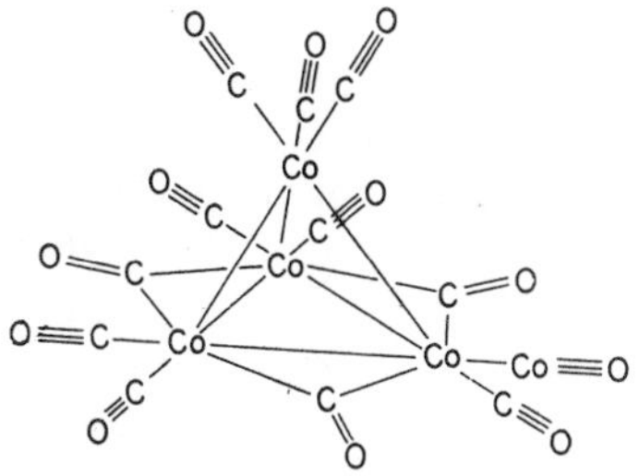

VII

bond (2·52 Å), it is concluded that this is also present, thus bringing the electronic structure of each iron atom up to that of the next inert gas and accounting for the diamagnetism (V). The structure of the trimeric tetra-carbonyl, $Fe_3(CO)_{12}$, has been shown to be based on an equilateral triangular arrangement of iron atoms, each probably with an octahedral environment completed by four carbonyl groups (VI), as in the corresponding osmium compound, $Os_3(CO)_{12}$.

When heated to 50°C cobalt octacarbonyl loses carbon monoxide giving a black, highly reactive, tetrameric carbonyl, $Co_4(CO)_{12}$, which has been found to have a pyramidal structure (VII) with metal–metal bonds and both terminal and bridging carbonyl groups.

An exception to the inert-gas structure of simple carbonyls is provided by vanadium carbonyl, $V(CO)_6$, which can be obtained by the action of carbon monoxide on vanadium cyclopentadienyl. This has one electron less than chromium carbonyl and could be expected to dimerize. However, the solid compound is paramagnetic and presumably the monomeric unit is prevented from dimerization by co-ordinate saturation of the metal atom. As might be expected, this compound is very reactive. It is easily reduced to salts of the $[V(CO)_6]^-$ ion and reacts with nitric oxide to give $[V(CO)_5(NO)]^\circ$; the ion and this molecule are isoelectronic with chromium carbonyl. It also reacts with triphenylphosphine to give the compound $(Ph_3P)_2V(CO)_4$, but nitrogenous bases bring about oxidation with the formation of salts of the type $[V^{II}(NR_3)_6][V(CO)_6]_2$.

Although insoluble in water, iron and cobalt carbonyls dissolve in alkalis, and on acidification give the carbonyl hydrides, $H_2Fe(CO)_4$ and $HCo(CO)_4$, as volatile liquids decomposing a little above room temperatures. Investigation of their structures by electron diffraction shows that the four —CO groups are arranged tetrahedrally about the metal atom as in nickel carbonyl, one of the Co—C bond lengths in the cobalt compound being longer (1·83 Å) than the other three (1·75 Å); as the infrared absorption shows no bands characteristic of the —OH group, it is concluded that the hydrogen atom is linked to the other three —CO groups by multi-centre bonds involving the non-bonding electrons on the oxygen atoms or, perhaps, the bonding electrons of the —C≡O group (VIII). As might be expected, the hydrogen atoms in these carbonyl hydrides are acidic, the anions $[Fe(CO)_4]^{2-}$ and $[Co(CO)_4]^-$ being isoelectronic with nickel carbonyl. The salts, particularly those of heavy metals, are readily obtained by the action of salts of these metals on solutions of

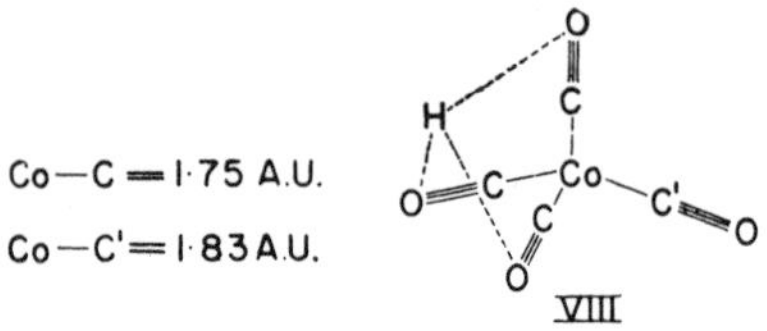

Co—C = 1·75 A.U.
Co—C' = 1·83 A.U.

VIII

the carbonyls in alkali or ammonia, and in a few cases direct syntheses of these salts have been achieved, for example that of the zinc salt,

$Zn[Co(CO)_4]_2$, by heating cobalt bromide and finely divided zinc with carbon monoxide under pressure.

Carbonyl anions have now been shown to be present in several of the ammine–carbonyls formed by the action of amines on carbonyls. Thus the compounds formerly represented as $Fe_4(CO)_{11}(en)_3$, $Fe_3(CO)_8(en)_3$ and $Fe_2(CO)_4(en)_3$, obtained by the action of ethylenediamine (en) on iron tetracarbonyl at successively higher temperatures, are now thought to be salts of the tris-ethylenediamine ferrous ion with the carbonyl anions $[Fe_3(CO)_{11}]^{2-}$, $[Fe_2(CO)_8]^{2-}$ and $[Fe(CO)_4]^{2-}$; in the same way, the action of ammonia on mercuric cobalt carbonyl, $Hg[Co(CO)_4]_2$, gives $Co_3(CO)_8(NH_3)_6$, now recognized as the salt $[Co(NH_3)_6][Co(CO)_4]_2$.

The carbonyl halides, $Fe(CO)_2X_2$, $Fe(CO)_4X_2$ and $Fe(CO)_5X_2$, formed by the action of halogens on iron carbonyl or the carbonyl salts, such as $Hg[Fe(CO)_4]$, however, cannot be of this type as they are soluble and monomeric in organic solvents. The structures of those with two and five carbonyl groups are unknown, but the tetracarbonyl halides are presumably octahedral molecules. It is significant that the iodides are the most stable of these compounds, as we should expect if the non-bonding electrons on the iron atom are to be available for back co-ordination to the carbonyl groups.

Reaction of carbonyl anions with organic halogen compounds has led to the synthesis of some compounds in which the organic group is attached direct to the metal atom. Thus, sodium tetracarbonyl cobalt with methyl iodide or benzyl bromide gives methyl or benzyl cobalt carbonyl:

$$Co(CO)_4^- + RX \rightarrow RCo(CO)_4 + X^-$$

and analogous compounds have been obtained by reaction of the pentacarbonyl rhenium ion with alkyl halides and also with carboxylic acid halides.

The alkyl halides in this type of reaction can be replaced by covalent metal halides in which the metal is also attached to phosphorus or arsenic. Thus, by reaction of triphenylphosphinegold(I) chloride with carbonyl anions, a series of metal–metal bonded compounds is obtained:

$$\begin{array}{l} Ph_3PAu.Mn(CO)_5 \\ Ph_3PAu.Co(CO)_4 \\ (Ph_3PAu)_2.Fe(CO)_4 \\ Ph_3PAu.V(CO)_6 \end{array}$$

The last of these compounds, which is a solid, diamagnetic and stable in air provides a remarkable example of 7:co-ordinate vanadium. Another example of a metal–metal bonded compound is the enneacarbonyl produced by pyrolysis at 60°C of the salt $[Re(CO)_6]^+ [Co(CO)_4]^-$.

$$[Re(CO)_6]^+ [Co(CO)_4]^- \rightarrow (CO)_5Re.Co(CO)_4 + CO$$

*ISO*NITRILES AND PHOSPHORUS COMPLEXES

The —CO group in the carbonyls can be replaced by a number of other groups, which are able to allow back co-ordination of the *d*-electrons of the metal atom. Among these are the *iso*nitriles, RNC; thus, iron pentacarbonyl reacts with *iso*nitriles giving compounds of the type $Fe(CO)_3(CNR)_2$ and chromium carbonyl gives $Cr(CO)_3(CNR)_3$. Hexa*iso*nitriles of chromium, molybdenum and tungsten are obtained by reaction between aryl*iso*cyanides and chromous acetate or the covalent halides of the heavier metals (IX).

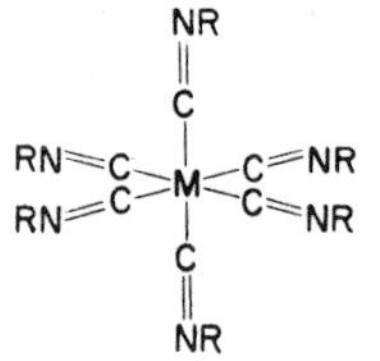

IX

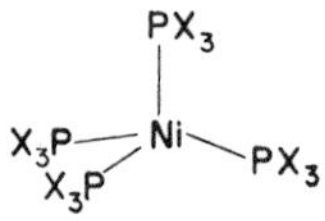

X

In the same way, trivalent phosphorus compounds (but not the corresponding nitrogen compounds, as the nitrogen atom cannot accept back co-ordinated electrons) react with nickel carbonyl to give tetra-tri-substituted-phosphine nickels (X); compounds of this type are known with a wide range of phosphorus compounds and one of them, $Ni(PCl_2Me)_4$, has been obtained by the direct action of boiling dichloromethylphosphine on nickel turnings.

One of the most remarkable effects of co-ordination of phosphorus compounds is the stabilization of transition metal hydrido complexes. Thus, the reaction of potassium tetrachloroplatinate(II) and alkali with triphenyl phosphine in alcohol gives a series of compounds, $PtH_2(PPh_3)_4$, $PtH_2(PPh_3)_3$, $PtH_2(PPh_3)_2$ and a variety of analogous hydrido complexes can be obtained by reduction of transition metal phosphine halides by sodium borohydride. These include halogen-containing complexes such as $PtHBr(PEt_3)_2$ obtained by reduction of dibromo-bis(triethylphosphine)platinum(II). This compound has been shown by X-ray analysis to have a *trans*-square-planar configuration and the reaction is best regarded as a substitution of the co-ordinated halide ion by a co-ordinated hydride ion.

Although the most stable hydrido compounds are those in which the metal atom is also co-ordinated to phosphorus or arsenic, stabilization of the metal–hydride linkage can also be achieved by carbonyl or cyclopentadienyl groups and a number of compounds is known in which even these groups are not necessary; for example, the rhodium ethylenediamine hydride ion $[Rh^{III}en_2H_2]^+$ and the remarkable complex hydrides K_2ReH_8 and K_2TcH_8 obtained by reduction of rhenium or technetium complexes with potassium in liquid ammonia.

NITROSYLS

The principle of maintenance of the effective atomic number of the metal atom in carbonyl-like compounds is well illustrated by the reactions of iron enneacarbonyl and cobalt carbonyl with nitric oxide, which forms the mixed carbonyl–nitrosyls $Fe(CO)_2(NO)_2$ and $Co(CO)_2(NO)$.† These substances have simple tetrahedral molecules with linear M—C—O and M—N—O groups, and since the replacement of a —CO group by —NO involves an increase of one electron in the system, are both isoelectronic with nickel carbonyl. As in nickel carbonyl, the M—C and M—N bonds are shortened, indicating some degree of double-bonding by back co-ordination from the metal atoms.

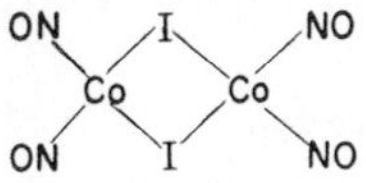

XI 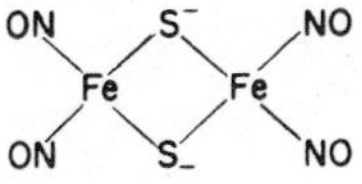 XII

Ferrous and cobaltous halides, particularly the iodides, also react with nitric oxide, giving compounds of the type $M(NO)_2X$. The iron compounds are very reactive, but those of cobalt, which melt at 100–130°C, are stable to air and react only slowly with water; their structure is unknown, but the dimeric halogen-bridged formula (XI) has been proposed as preserving the effective atomic number of 36 on the cobalt atoms. The related structure (XII) has been proposed for the anion $[Fe_2(NO)_4S_2]^{2-}$, found in the diamagnetic Roussin's red salts, which are obtained when nitric oxide reacts with ferrous salts in the presence of a sulphide, and the Roussin's black salts first formed are treated with alkali.

NITROPRUSSIDES AND COMPLEX ACETYLIDES

In the carbonyls and analogous compounds so far described the metal atoms are characterized by a formal valency state zero. The —CO, —NO

†A third member of this series, $Mn(CO)(NO)_3$, has now been obtained.

and related groups can, however, also be introduced into co-ordination compounds of the transition metals in their usual valency states. For example, carbon monoxide reacts with a hot ferrocyanide solution to give the anion, $[Fe(CN)_5(CO)]^{3-}$, of carbonylferrocyanic acid, which can be isolated from the acidified solution as a pale yellow crystalline hydrate, $H_3[Fe(CN)_5(CO)].H_2O$. Another example is the red-brown "nitroprusside", $K_2[Fe(CN)_5(NO)]$, obtained when potassium ferrocyanide is heated with 5 N nitric acid, and familiar for its colour reactions with sulphides (purple) and reactive methylene groups (red in alkaline solution, turning green on acidification).

From their formulae the "nitroprussides" appear to be nitrosoferricyanides with trivalent iron, but their diamagnetism shows that they must be derivatives of ferrous iron (krypton structure in octahedral complexes) with the nitric oxide co-ordinated as NO^+, the odd electron of the nitric oxide molecule being transferred to the iron atom:

	3*d*					4*s*	4*p*			
$[Fe^{III}(CN)_6]^{3-}$	⇅	⇅	↓	⇅ CN	⇅ CN	⇅ CN	⇅ CN	⇅ CN	⇅ CN	paramagnetic
$[Fe^{III}(CN)_5(NO)]^{2-}$	⇅	⇅	↓	⇅ N •O	⇅ CN	⇅ CN	⇅ CN	⇅ CN	⇅ CN	paramagnetic
$[Fe^{II}(CN)_5(\overset{+}{NO})]^{2-}$	⇅	⇅	⇅	⇅ N +O	⇅ CN	⇅ CN	⇅ CN	⇅ CN	⇅ CN	diamagnetic
$[Fe^{II}(CN)_5(CO)]^{3-}$	⇅	⇅	⇅	⇅ CO	⇅ CN	⇅ CN	⇅ CN	⇅ CN	⇅ CN	diamagnetic

The groups CN^-, CO and NO^+ are isoelectronic and the complex ions $[Fe(CN)_6]^{4-}$, $[Fe(CN)_5(CO)]^{3-}$, and $[Fe(CN)_5(\overset{+}{NO})]^{2-}$ differ only in the nuclear charges (atomic numbers) of the atoms in the sixth ligand. Also isoelectronic with these ions is the acetylide ion, C_2^{2-}, and within the past ten years a considerable range of complex acetylides has been obtained.

The simple acetylides are all very unstable, but replacement of one of the hydrogen atoms of acetylene by an alkyl, or better, aryl group considerably increases the stability. In liquid ammonia solution, for example, ferrous thiocyanate and potassium acetylides give the hexa-acetylido complexes, $K_4[Fe(C_2R)_6]$, and nickel hexammine thiocyanate gives tetra-acetylido complexes, $K_2[Ni(C_2R)_4]$, analogous to the normal complex cyanide of divalent nickel.

While the monosubstituted acetylenes have an acidic hydrogen atom and consequently form donor anions of the type RC_2^-, as in the above examples, disubstituted acetylenes cannot do this. Nevertheless, some

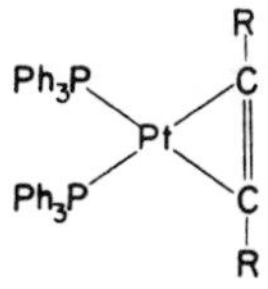

XIII

complexes are known in which disubstituted acetylenes act as ligands, for example the platinum compounds $[(Ph_3P)_2Pt(C_2R_2)]$, obtained by reduction of *cis*-$[(Ph_3P)_2PtCl_2]$ in the presence of the acetylenes. These complexes, in which the platinum appears to be zero-valent are most stable when the acetylene is substituted by aryl groups; the acetylene molecules apparently act as bidentate ligands in agreement with the observation that the infra-red absorption shows the triple bond to have been opened (XIII).

OLEFIN COMPLEXES

Chloroplatinites react with olefins in two stages, a chloride ion being replaced by a molecule of the olefin at each stage. Thus, with ethylene:

$$[PtCl_4]^{2-} \rightarrow [PtCl_3(C_2H_4)]^- \rightarrow [PtCl_2(C_2H_4)_2]^\circ$$

Formation of the mono-olefin salt, known as Zeise's salt, is shown by the colour change of the chloroplatinite solution from red to yellow; extraction of this yellow aqueous solution with ether gives the neutral compound $[PtCl_2(C_2H_4)]_2$, containing one less ethylene group attached to each platinum atom and shown by depression of freezing point in benzene to be dimeric and by dipole moment methods to have the *trans*-planar bridged structure (XIV). Other olefins can be used instead of ethylene,

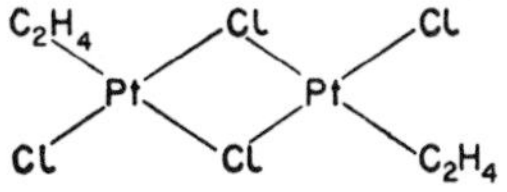

XIV 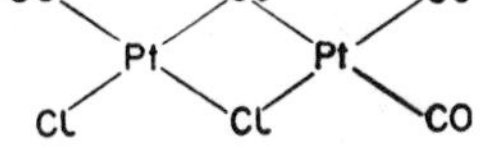 XV

but the complexes are less stable, being decomposed in some cases even by carbon monoxide, with the formation of the carbonyl chlorides, $[PtCl_3CO]^-$ and $[PtCl_2CO]_2$ (XV). All of these compounds are decomposed by cyanide with the formation of platinocyanide, $[Pt(CN)_4]^{2-}$, and quantitative liberation of olefin or carbon monoxide.

The ethylene complexes were originally thought to contain bonds of this type:

$$Pt \leftarrow CH_2 \leftarrow CH_2$$

but infrared absorption indicates that the symmetry of the olefin molecules is retained and X-ray analysis shows that the olefin is bound to the platinum by "sideways" co-ordination, the fourth co-ordination position of the platinum being taken by the centre of the C=C double bond (XVI). Chatt has suggested that the bonding involves co-ordination of the π-electrons of the double bond to the platinum atom and that the strength of the bond is reinforced by "back co-ordination" of non-bonding electrons on the platinum atom (possibly in *dp*-hybrid orbitals) to the antibonding π-orbital of the olefin molecule (XVII).

Olefin complexes of this type are also known in which a doubly unsaturated molecule behaves as a bidentate ligand, filling two co-ordination positions on the metal atom and being bound by co-ordination

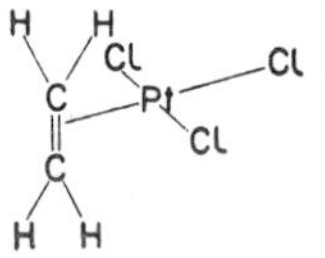

XVI

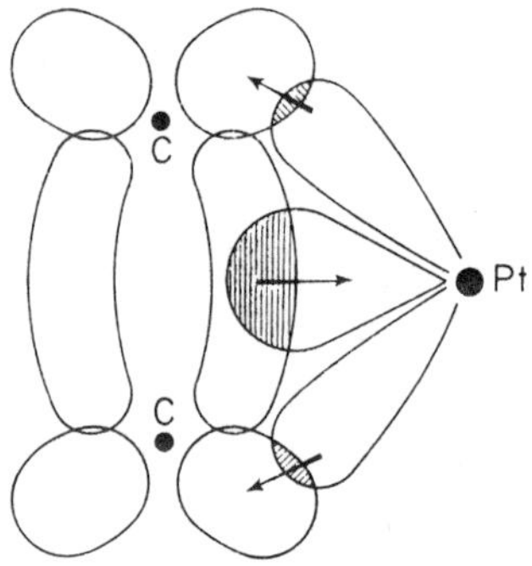

XVII

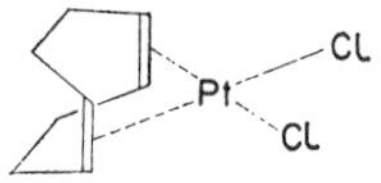

XVIII

of the π-electrons of the double bond in each position; the *cyclo*octa-1:5-diene complexes (XVIII) being particularly stable.

*CYCLO*PENTADIENYLS AND RELATED COMPOUNDS

In 1951 unsuccessful attempts to oxidize *cyclo*pentadienyl magnesium bromide (XXI) to di*cyclo*pentadienyl (XXII) with ferric chloride in solution in organic solvents resulted in the isolation of an iron derivative, $FeC_{10}H_{10}$, an orange solid, m.p. 173°C, soluble in organic solvents, at first formulated as a normal organometallic compound (XXIII). About the same time this compound was also obtained by the direct reaction between *cyclo*pentadiene and a reduced iron catalyst at 350–400°C.

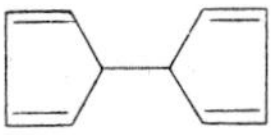

Fe

CH_2MgBr

XXII 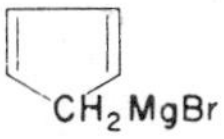 XXI 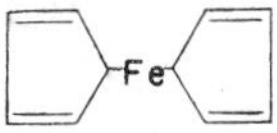 XXIII

The development of synthetic methods has now led to the preparation of similar compounds of many other metals, mostly of the form $MC_{10}H_{10}$, isomorphous with the iron compound and melting within a few degrees of the same temperature. All these compounds clearly have similar molecular structures and the observation that all have zero dipole moment and show only one type of C—H absorption in the infrared is interpreted as indicating a "sandwich" type of structure (XXIV), subsequently confirmed by electron diffraction and X-ray analysis of the iron compound, which has, in the solid state, ten equal Fe—C distances of 2·04 Å and ten equal C—C distances of 1·40 Å. This C—C distance corresponds to that in benzene, and if these compounds are regarded as formed by co-ordination of two *cyclo*pentadienyl anions (C_5H^-) to a divalent cation, this can be readily understood, as the "aromatic" nature of the $C_5H_5^-$ ion is familiar to the organic chemist.

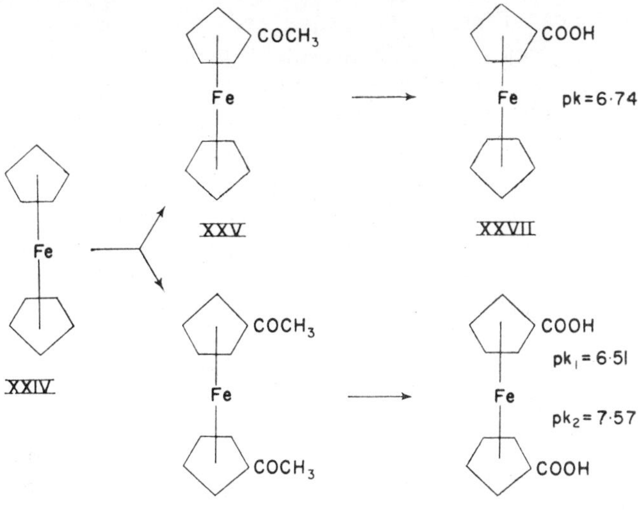

$COCH_3$ $COOH$

Fe Fe pk = 6·74

XXV XXVII

Fe

$COCH_3$ $COOH$

$pk_1 = 6·51$

XXIV

Fe Fe

$pk_2 = 7·57$

$COCH_3$ $COOH$

XXVI XXVIII

The iron compound was thus regarded as the first member of a new series of aromatic compounds and named "ferrocene". Its aromatic character is shown by a number of reactions in which it undergoes ring substitution, under conditions similar to those commonly leading to substitution in benzene.

Thus, Friedel–Crafts acylation is brought about by the action of acetyl chloride and aluminium chloride, mono- and di-acetyl derivatives being obtained (XXV, XXVI), which can be reduced to ethyl derivatives or oxidized to carboxylic acids (XXVII, XXVIII); these acids are comparable in strength to benzoic acid (p*k*, under similar conditions, = 6·62) and the very small difference between the first and second dissociation constants of the dicarboxylic acid shows that the carboxyl groups are in separate rings.

Although sulphonation can be carried out in acetic anhydride solution, giving mono- and di-sulphonic acids, more vigorous substituting agents, such as nitric acid or halogens, oxidize the ferrocene to blue salts of the "ferricinium" cation, $Fe(C_5H_5)_2^+$, in which the iron is trivalent; the positive charge on this cation then makes substitution impossible. The ferricinium salts, easily obtained in this way, can be reduced back to ferrocene by, for example, stannous chloride. A value of +0·30 V is quoted for the oxidation potential of the $Fe(C_5H_5)_2^+/Fe(C_5H_5)_2$ couple, comparable to that for the ferricyanide/ferrocyanide couple.

The direct action of *cyclo*pentadiene on metals is only an effective method of preparing *cyclo*pentadienyls in the case of iron, and since the formation of ferrocene from the Grignard reagent of *cyclo*pentadiene and ferric chloride clearly depends upon the homogeneity of the reaction, general methods of preparation have been based on the use of co-ordination compounds of the metals, soluble in organic solvents.

Benzene- or ether-soluble complexes of several metals have been found to react with the Grignard reagent, *cyclo*pentadienyl magnesium bromide, to give *cyclo*pentadienyls. Nickel acetylacetonate, for example, gives nickel *cyclo*pentadienyl, $Ni(C_5H_5)_2$, as dark green crystals, m.p. 127°C, and vanadium tetrachloride gives the vanadium compound, $V(C_5H_5)_2$, m.p. 168°C, dark violet. Under the same conditions cobaltic acetylacetonate gives the cobaltic cation, $Co(C_5H_5)_2^+$, isoelectronic with ferrocene and stable in aqueous solution from which the anions of some very strong acids precipitate insoluble salts, such as the tetraphenylborate, $[Co(C_5H_5)_2]^+ [BPh_4]^-$.

The cobalticinium ion, $Co(C_5H_5)_2^+$, resists all attempts at reduction to cobaltocene, $Co(C_5H_5)_2$. This compound has, however, been made by the reaction between tetrammine cobaltous thiocyanate and lithium *cyclo*pentadienyl in liquid ammonia: the salt $[Co(NH_3)_6]^{2+}2C_5H_5^-$ first obtained decomposes on heating *in vacuo,* giving a sublimate of dark violet cobaltocene, very easily oxidized to the cobalticinium ion (compare other complexes of divalent cobalt, such as $Co(CN)_6^{4-}$). The bright red chromium compound, $Cr(C_5H_5)_2$, can be similarly obtained via the salt

$[Cr(NH_3)_6](C_5H_5)_3$, and reaction of ferric chloride with indenyl lithium in ether gives bis-indenyl iron (XXIX), a purple solid, m.p. 185°C.

2 Li$^{\oplus}$ → Fe → Fe

XXIX XXX

The aromatic character of the *cyclo*pentadienyl ring is decreased by fusion of the benzene ring (compare naphthalene) and oxidation of the indenyl compound cannot be accomplished without destruction of the molecule; hydrogenation, however, preferentially reduces the benzene ring and the orange bis-tetrahydroindenyl iron (XXX) obtained can readily be oxidized to the blue cation $Fe(C_9H_{11})_2^+$.

By the action of the more reactive sodium *cyclo*pentadienyl on manganese bromide in tetrahydrofuran as solvent, the manganese compound, $Mn(C_5H_5)_2$ has been obtained. This compound exists in two different modifications: at ordinary temperatures it is a brown solid with a magnetic moment of about 1β (β = Bohr's magneton); as the temperature rises the magnetic moment changes gradually, reaching a maximum of about $5{\cdot}8\beta$ above 160°C, the change being accompanied by a loss of the brown

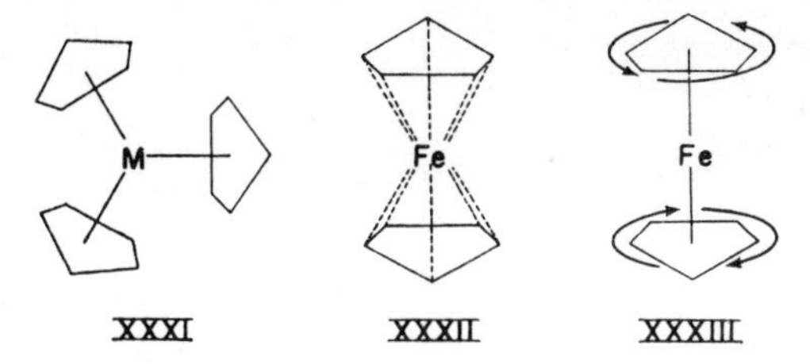

colour; the white form produced melts sharply at 173°C and can be preserved by rapid cooling. This peculiar change in properties is analogous to a change from low-spin to high-spin electronic configuration. This method of preparation, using the sodium *cyclo*pentadienyl in tetrahydrofuran, has also given a series of *cyclo*pentadienyls of the lanthanide elements of the form $M(C_5H_5)_3$, probably with the structure (XXXI), the three metal–ring links being coplanar at angles of 120°.

Electronic Structure of the Cyclopentadienyls

The iron atom has eight electrons in its valency shell, which can accommodate eighteen; since the $C_5H_5\cdot$ radical has five electrons in excess of those involved in the interatomic σ-bonds, the earlier descriptions of the ferrocene molecule envisaged the co-ordination of all these electrons to complete the inert-gas structure of the iron atom, the bonding being, in effect, by five one-electron Fe—C bonds to each ring (XXXII). The failure to isolate isomeric forms of the disubstituted ferrocenes, such as (XXVI) and (XXVIII), and other evidence for the free rotation of the rings about the line of centres has led, however, to the rejection of this structure in favour of one in which the *cyclo*pentadienyl rings are bound to the metal atom by π-bonds (XXXIII).

The *cyclo*pentadienyls can then be regarded either as π-bound complexes of the $C_5H_5\cdot$ radicals with the neutral metal atom or as complexes of the anions, $C_5H_5^-$, with the divalent metal cation. The aromatic character of the ring in these compounds suggests that the latter approach is preferable.

The $C_5H_5^-$ anion has an "aromatic sextet" of non-σ-bonding electrons, the lowest energy molecular orbitals of which are as follows:

(1) A Σ-orbital, spheroidal in shape and extending over the whole molecule, analogous to an atomic *s*-orbital (XXXIV).

(2) Two Π-orbitals, broadly dumbbell-shaped, oriented at right angles to one another, and analogous to atomic *p*-orbitals (XXXV, XXXVI):

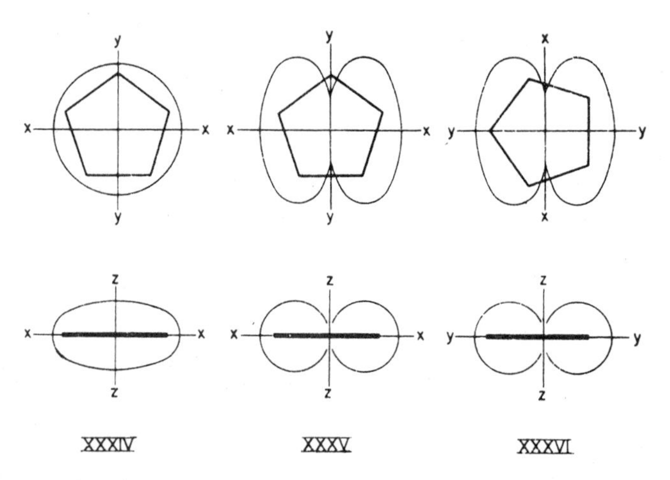

Plans and elevations of the molecular orbitals of the *cyclo*pentadienyl anion

In the $C_5H_5^-$ ion all of these lowest orbitals are doubly occupied; the two Π-orbitals, which are of equal energy (i.e. degenerate), provide the bonding electrons.

The iron atom is oriented with the *z*-axis in the line of centres of the two rings and the electrostatic repulsion of the non-bonding electrons in the *cyclo*pentadienyl Σ-orbital raises the energy of the atomic d_{z^2}-orbital so far, that hybridization with the 4*s*-orbital can occur, producing two new, more compact, hybrid *ds*-orbitals, one of which is of lower energy than the original d_{z^2}-orbital, and one of higher. The atomic orbitals, in order of increasing energy, thus become:

high *ds*-hybrid	——	$(4s, 3d)\sigma_+$
$3d_{xz}, 3d_{yz}$	—— ——	$3d\pi$
low *ds*-hybrid	——	$(4s, 3d)\sigma$
$3d_{xy}, 3d_{x^2-y^2}$	—— ——	$3d\delta$

Energy levels of atomic orbitals in complexes of ferrocene type

Bond formation occurs mainly by co-ordination of the electrons in the Π-orbitals of the *cyclo*pentadienyl anions to the $3d\pi$ orbitals of the metal atom, which have suitable symmetry (XXXVII). In ferrocene, therefore, the six original electrons of the ferrous ion are paired in the three lowest atomic orbitals (two $3d\delta$ and σ_-) and four more electrons are donated from the *cyclo*pentadienyl anion Π-orbitals to the metallic $3d\pi$-orbitals. The molecule thus has all of its electrons paired and is diamagnetic. Oxidation to the ferricinium ion removes one electron (probably from the σ_--orbital) giving a paramagnetic ion with one uncompensated spin ($\mu = 2{\cdot}26\beta$). The chromium and vanadium compounds

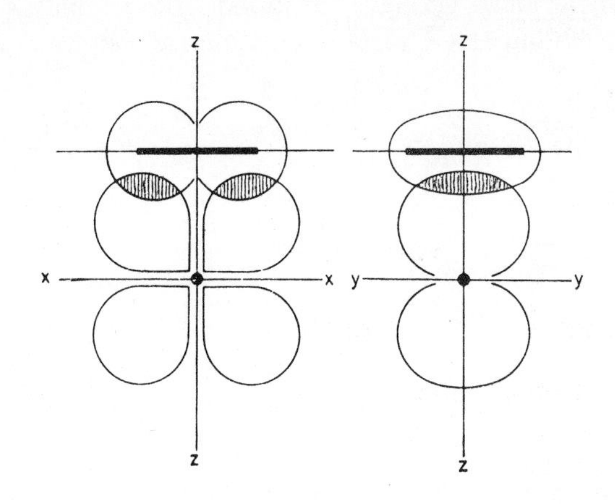

XXXVII

Front and side views of overlap between the Π_x-orbital of the *cyclo*pentadienyl anion and the $3d_{xz}$-orbital of the metal ion

are also paramagnetic with two and three unpaired electrons, respectively, as expected, and the magnetic properties of the other *cyclo*pentadienyls can be interpreted in a similar manner.

The "Chromium Phenyls" and Related Compounds

The "sandwich" structure of the *cyclo*pentadienyls is the result of co-ordination to a metal ion of the π-electrons of an aromatic system and similar compounds can be expected with other aromatic systems, in particular with benzene itself, of which the chromium compound, $Cr(C_6H_6)_2$, would be isoelectronic with ferrocene, and so likely to be the most stable compound of this type.

Chromium phenyl halides of the form $Cr(Ph)_nX$ were obtained by Hein as early as 1919 by the action of phenyl magnesium bromide on anhydrous chromic chloride in organic solvents. Electrolytic reduction of these salts gave the diamagnetic "chromium phenyls", $CrPh_3$ and $CrPh_4$, since shown by reduction with lithium aluminium deuteride to contain, respectively, one and two diphenyl groups and so to be formulated $Cr(C_6H_6)(C_{12}H_{10})$ and $Cr(C_{12}H_{10})_2$. The simplest member of the series, dibenzene chromium, $Cr(C_6H_6)_2$, has been prepared from the reaction of chromium chloride with aluminium chloride, aluminium and benzene at high temperature: hydrolysis of the reaction mixture gives the salt $Cr(C_6H_6)_2^+Cl^-$, which is reduced by hydrosulphite to black, diamagnetic dibenzene chromium, melting at 284°C, decomposing a little above its melting point into chromium and benzene, and shown by X-ray analysis to have a "sandwich" structure (XXXVIII).

In this method of preparation benzene can be replaced by other aromatic hydrocarbons, giving substituted compounds, such as bis-mesitylene chromium (XXXIX) from mesitylene and bis-diphenyl

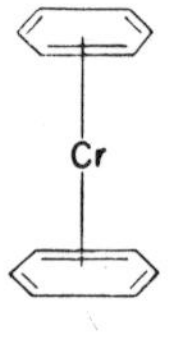

Cr Cr Cr

Me Me Me Me Me Me

XXXVIII 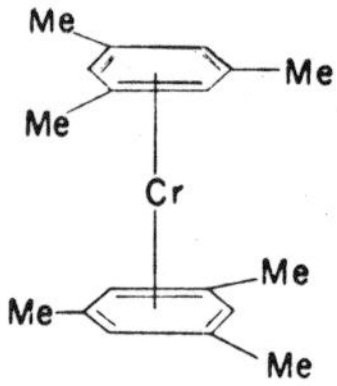 XXXIX 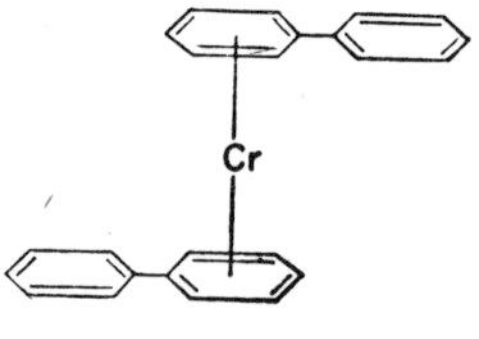 XL

chromium (XL) from diphenyl; this last compound can be oxidized to a cation, $Cr(C_{12}H_{10})_2^+$, the iodide of which is identical with Hein's "tetraphenyl chromium iodide". From rhenium pentachloride the same method of preparation gave salts of the corresponding bis-aryl rhenium cations, $Re(Ar)_2^+$, which could not be reduced; corresponding salts of the divalent cations $Fe(Ar)_2^{2+}$ have also been obtained; these ions are analogous to the cobalticinium ion in the *cyclo*pentadienyl series.

Since ferrocene, dibenzene chromium and the cations obtained with rhenium, iron and ruthenium are all isoelectronic, neutral "sandwich" molecules may be expected for the metals of group VII in combination with one aromatic ring and one *cyclo*pentadienyl anion, and a red, diamagnetic manganese compound of this type has been obtained by the action of phenyl magnesium bromide on methyl*cyclo*pentadienyl manganese chloride.

Theoretically any aromatic system should be able to form compounds with the "sandwich" structure, but in heterocyclic systems this type of π:co-ordination is usually prevented by the preference of the ligand for normal co-ordination via the hetero-atom; pyridine and other heterocyclic bases, for instance, always co-ordinate via the nitrogen atom. However, a few "sandwich" compounds are known with thiophenes as π-donors (the electronegativities of carbon and sulphur are not widely different, particularly when that of the sulphur is reduced by conjugation of the non-bonding pairs with the unsaturated system), and by blocking the donor properties of the nitrogen atom by quaternary salt formation, it has been possible to form "sandwich" compounds with pyridine.

Cyclopentadienyl Carbonyls

Reaction of the *cyclo*pentadienyls with carbon monoxide under pressure or of the carbonyls with *cyclo*pentadiene at elevated temperatures yields mixed carbonyl*cyclo*pentadienyls. Thus, by the action of carbon monoxide the *cyclo*pentadienyls of vanadium, manganese and cobalt give the mixed compounds $V(C_5H_5)(CO)_4$, $Mn(C_5H_5)(CO)_3$ and $Co(C_5H_5)(CO)_2$. These compounds are all monomeric and diamagnetic, suggesting analogy with the carbonyls of the alternate elements chromium, iron and nickel; and if the *cyclo*pentadiene ion, $C_5H_5^-$, is considered as donating *all* its π-electrons the metals in these mixed compounds have, as in the carbonyls, the electronic structure of the next inert gas. The

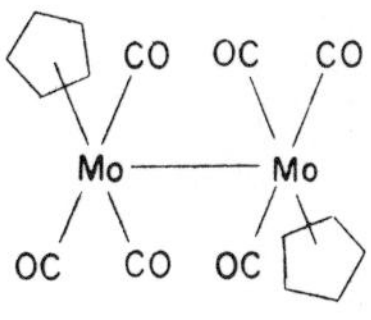

XLII

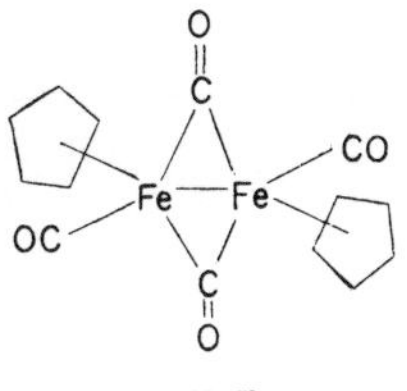

XLI

expected formation of dimeric *cyclo*pentadienylcarbonyls by the intervening elements is illustrated by the compounds $[Cr(C_5H_5)(CO)_3]_2$, $[Mo(C_5H_5)(CO)_3]_2$, $[W(C_5H_5)(CO)_3]_2$ and $[Fe(C_5H_5)(CO)_3]_2$ (XLI). The molybdenum compound has been shown to have direct Mo—Mo bonds linking the two halves of the dimer (XLII).

A number of related compounds is also known in which some of the —CO groups are replaced by the isoelectronic —NO^+ or CN^- or by

PX_3 molecules, for example the nickel compound $(C_5H_5)Ni(NO)$, isoelectronic with the unknown $Cu(C_5H_5)(CO)$, which would be the terminal member of the series of *cyclo*pentadienylcarbonyls formed by vanadium, manganese and cobalt. There is also a variety of compounds known in which *cyclo*pentadienyl groups are accompanied by hydrides.

Extensive studies of the reactions of carbonyls and *cyclopentadienyls* has revealed a bewildering variety of metal complexes of the π-arene type. Thus reaction of iron pentacarbonyl with dimethylacetylene gives a compound at first formulated $Fe(CO)_5(CH_3C{:}CCH_3)_2$, but since shown to be a π-complex of duroquinone (XLIII), formed by condensation of the acetylene with carbon monoxide.

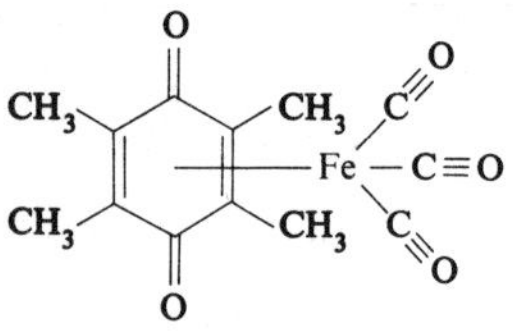

XLIII 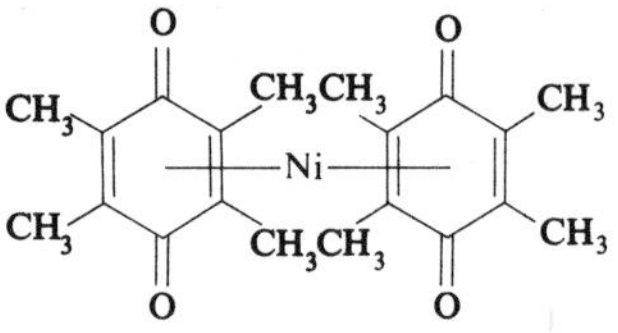 XLIV

A nickel π-duroquinone complex (XLIV) can be obtained by reaction of nickel carbonyl with duroquinone. When dimethylacetylene reacts with iron carbonyl hydride, however, a different type of condensation occurs, giving the complex (XLV) in which one iron atom forms part of a chelate ring, and the other is linked to it by a metal–metal bond and also to the chelate ring by a π-bond.

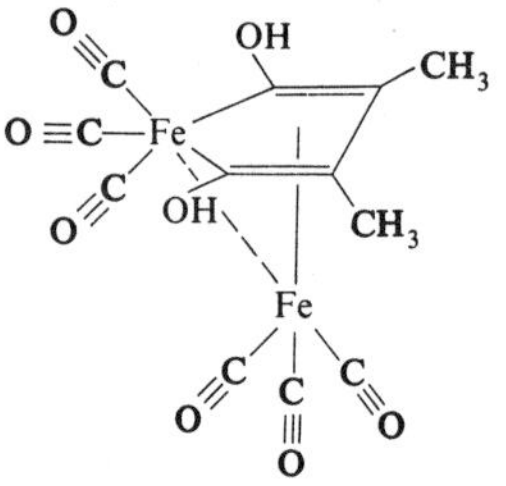

XLV 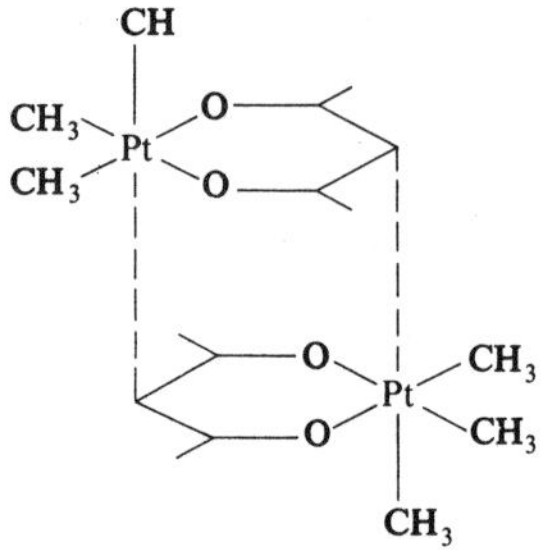 XLVI

Another example of π-bonding by a chelate ring is provided by the compound (XLVI) obtained when acetylacetone reacts with platinum trimethyl. The linkage from the central carbon atom of the ring to the neighbouring platinum atom recalls the association between neighbouring molecules in bis(acetylacetonato)copper(II) (Chapter III, Fig. XXXI).

FURTHER READING

COATES, G. E., *Organo-Metallic Compounds*, 2nd ed., Methuen, London (1960).

ABEL, E. W., The metal carbonyls, *Quart. Rev.* **17**, 133 (1963).
BENNETT, M. A., Olefin and acetylene complexes of transition metals, *Chem. Rev.* **62**, 611 (1962).
CABLE, J. W. and SHELINE, R. K., Bond hybridization and structure in the metal carbonyls, *Chem. Rev.* **56**, 1 (1956).
COTTON, F. A., Alkyls and aryls of the transition metals, *Chem. Rev.* **55**, 551 (1955).
IRVING, R. J., Nitric oxide and the metal nitrosyls, *Rec. Chem. Prog.* **26**, 115 (1965).
MALATESTA, L., Isocyanide complexes of the metals, *Progress Inorg. Chem.* **1**, 283 (1959).
PAUSON, P. L., Ferrocene and related compounds, *Quart. Rev.* **9**, 391 (1955).
STONE, F. G. A., Fluorocarbon derivatives of metals, *Advances Organometallic Chem.* **1**, 43 (1964).
WILKINSON, G. and COTTON, F. A., Cyclopentadienyls and arene–metal compounds, *Progress Inorg. Chem.* **1**, 1 (1959).

CHAPTER VII

SOME PRACTICAL APPLICATIONS

THOUGH many of the most recent advances in co-ordination chemistry have yet to find industrial uses, complex salts have a long history of practical significance. Of course, in many of the earliest applications, such as the dissolution of gold in aqua regia or the refinement of platinum by precipitation of potassium chloroplatinate, it was more or less of an accident that complex compounds were involved, and no deliberate attempt was made to utilize their special properties.

Amongst these, largely accidental, uses of co-ordination compounds some of the most important involve the complex fluorides of the lighter metals. Thus, in the production of metallic aluminium by the electrolytic reduction of alumina, the complex fluoride, Na_3AlF_6, which occurs naturally as the rather rare mineral cryolite, is used as a flux to lower the working temperature. Complex fluorides of beryllium, scandium, titanium, niobium and tantalum are also important metallurgically, largely because they are almost the only readily available compounds of these metals which resist hydrolysis. The differing resistance to hydrolysis of the complex fluoride ions of niobium, NbF_7^{2-}, and tantalum, TaF_7^{2-}, is the basis of the classical separation of these two very similar metals, the former being hydrolysed to the $NbOF_5^{2-}$ ion under conditions which do not affect the tantalum complex.

Where solubilities are low analytical applications may be possible and some common complex anions give very insoluble precipitates with metallic cations. Potassium ferrocyanide, for example, is used as a reagent for zinc, silver, copper, molybdenum, uranium and other metals because of the highly insoluble and, often, deeply coloured precipitates which are produced; the most familiar of these is the deep blue ferric salt, used as a pigment under the name "prussian blue". Satisfactory blue pigments and dyestuffs are peculiarly difficult to obtain and for many years prussian blue and the silicate pigment ultramarine were almost the only ones available. The discovery of copper phthalocyanin (monastral blue) has, however, now provided another blue pigment of outstanding properties and slight variations of shade are being obtained by substitution in the organic part of the molecule.

The characteristic colour of some co-ordination compounds has led to their use as colour tests in analysis. The well-known colour change of cobaltous solutions from pink to blue, for example, is due to the formation of complexes such as $CoCl_3^-$ and $CoCl_4^{2-}$, and more sensitive versions of this test are based on the formation of analogous complexes of higher stability, such as the thiocyanate complex obtained on addition of ammonium thiocyanate to cobaltous solutions, the blue colour in this case being extracted by organic solvents such as amyl alcohol. Other familiar examples are the red ferric thiocyanate complex and the blue cuprammine complex.

Numerous attempts have been made to find some application for the many metallic ammines, largely without success. Recently, however, it has been found that strong hydrochloric acid solutions of divalent cobalt can be quantitatively oxidized by oxygen and ammonia in the presence of activated charcoal, and highly purified cobalt can be made by recrystallization of the hexammine cobaltic chloride thus obtained. Ores containing cobalt, nickel and copper are also being extracted by selective leaching with ammonia solution under pressure, separation of the metals depending on the resistance of the various ammines so formed to reduction by hydrogen under pressure.

One of the peculiarities associated with co-ordination chemistry is the possibility of obtaining neutral, covalent, molecular, compounds of metals which, in their simple compounds, form ionic salts. These neutral compounds usually have low solubilities in water and are often readily volatile and may consequently be used in the separation of the metals concerned from contaminants. Familiar examples are the precipitation of divalent palladium as the diammine chloride, $Pd(NH_3)_2Cl_2$, the separation of the isotopes of uranium by the gaseous diffusion of the hexafluoride, and the refining of osmium and nickel by volatilization of the tetroxide and carbonyl, respectively.

INNER COMPLEXES

$Ni(CO)_4$, UF_6, and $Pd(NH_2)_2Cl_2$ are examples of neutral compounds in which the metal atoms are attached to simple ligands. Such compounds are comparatively few and often difficult to make, but an immense range of neutral compounds is accessible by the co-ordination of singly charged bidentate ligands. These anions form neutral complexes with cations having co-ordination numbers double their valency, such as Pd^{2+}, Cu^{2+}, Zn^{2+}, Al^{3+}, Cr^{3+}, Co^{3+} and Th^{4+} and many others. These neutral, chelate complexes are known as "inner" complexes.

Any organic chemist is familiar with the inner complexes formed by copper and the amino acids. On mixing hot solutions of cupric sulphate and sodium glycinate a deep blue-violet colour is produced which deposits

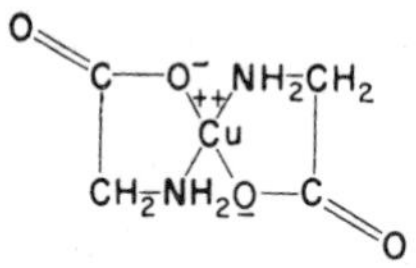

I

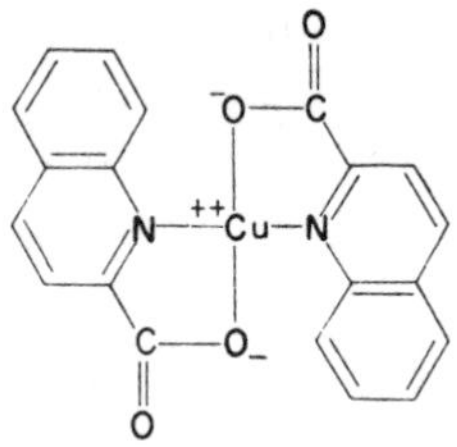

II

deep blue needles of cupric glycinate on cooling. The copper salt is sparingly soluble in cold water, almost a non-electrolyte and resistant to hydrolysis, though decomposed by acids. As early as 1904 Ley suggested the cyclic formula (I) for this compound and applied conductivity experiments to show the decreased stability of the six- and seven-membered rings formed by the anions of β-alanine and γ-aminobutyric acid. Whilst cupric glycinate and the α- and β-alaninates are appreciably soluble in water, the higher homologues become highly insoluble and have been used for the quantitative precipitation of copper, particularly good results being obtained with quinaldinic acid, the heterocyclic nitrogen and carboxylate anion acting as donors to form five-membered chelate rings (II).

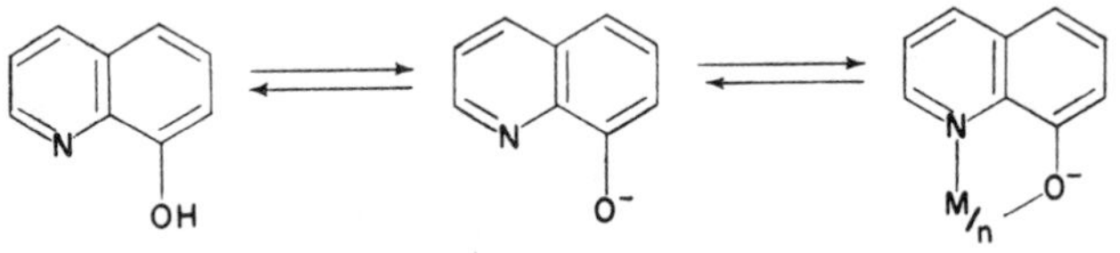

III IV V

Another example of the participation of a heterocyclic nitrogen atom in the chelate ring is provided by 8:hydroxyquinoline (III), "oxine", the anion of which (IV) co-ordinates with numerous metallic cations to give inner complexes (V). Since in acid solutions the metal and hydrogen ions are in direct competition for the oxinate anion and in alkaline solutions the oxinate and hydroxyl ions are in competition for the metal cation, there is a limited pH range of stability of the complex, characteristic for each metal, and dependent on the complex stability

TABLE 1. pH RANGES OF COMPLETE PRECIPITATION OF OXINATES

Cation	Cu^{2+}	Fe^{3+}	Al^{3+}	Zn^{2+}	Th^{4+}	Ti^{4+}	Mn^{2+}	Mg^{2+}	Ca^{2+}
pH range	$>2\cdot7$	$2\cdot8-11\cdot2$	$4\cdot2-9\cdot8$	$>4\cdot4$	$4\cdot4-8\cdot8$	$4\cdot8-8\cdot6$	$5\cdot9-10$	$>8\cdot2$	$>9\cdot2$

constants and the metal–hydroxyl ion association constants. These pH ranges, some values of which are given in Table 1, differ sufficiently for useful quantitative separations to be possible.

In practice oxine is most often used for the estimation of aluminium, zinc and magnesium (since alternative methods are available for transition metals), aluminium and zinc being precipitated at pH5, when magnesium remains in solution to be precipitated later from an ammoniacal chloride solution. In the presence of tartrate zinc may be precipitated while aluminium remains in solution and the extension of this type of control has made oxine one of the most versatile reagents, particularly as there are often alternative methods of completing the analysis: by weighing the precipitated complex after drying at 110°C, by igniting to the metal oxide and weighing this, or by solution in acid and estimation of the oxine in solution iodimetrically.

An important group of phenolic chelating agents is that in which the phenolic group has as neighbour a nitrosyl group. These compounds form particularly stable cobalt complexes, α-nitroso-β-naphthol (VI) being commonly used as a reagent for divalent cobalt, which forms the insoluble, red inner complex even in acetic acid solution. The inner complex (VII) can be solubilized by sulphonation of the naphthalene rings and the deep red colour produced in solution by combination of divalent cobalt with nitroso-R-salt (VIII) is a very sensitive test for this metal.

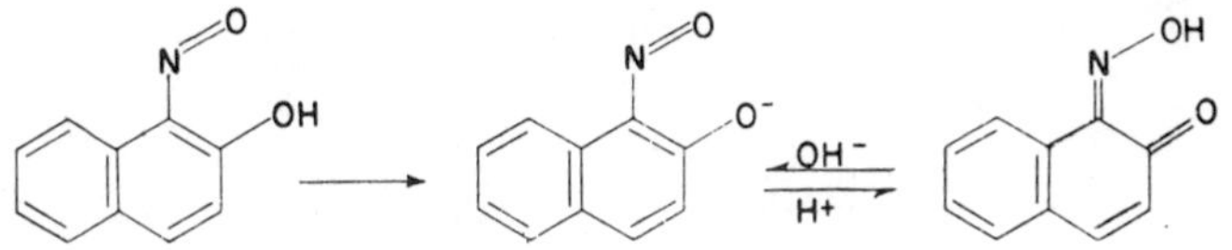

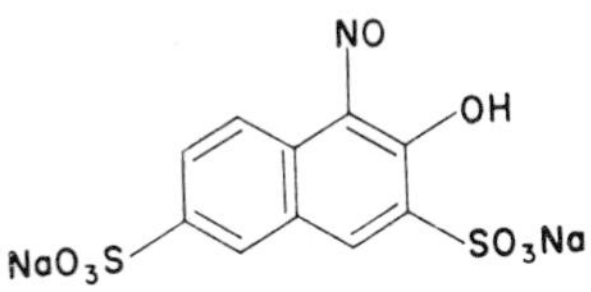

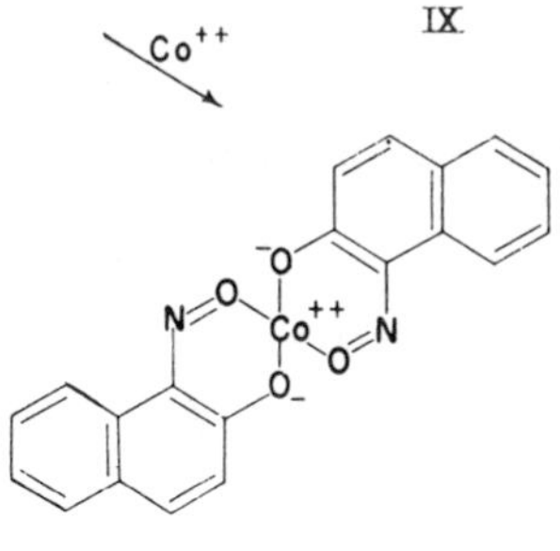

The nitrosophenols are tautomeric with the quinone monoximes (IX) and a number of other oximes with donor groups appropriately placed relative to the oxime group are capable of forming inner complexes.

Salicylaldoxime (X), for example, forms an insoluble cupric complex (XI) even in acidic solutions and a clean separation of copper from nickel is provided by the solubility of the nickel complex under these conditions, though it is quantitatively precipitated from ammoniacal solution. It will be noticed that the oxime group co-ordinates through the nitrogen atom. Oximes always co-ordinate in this way, as is shown by the behaviour of the stereoisomeric benzoinoximes. The α-oxime ("cupron") is a useful reagent for copper, giving a precipitate of the cupric inner complex in ammoniacal solutions; this isomer has the anti-configuration (XII), but the syn-isomer (β-benzoinoxime) has the hydroxyl group so placed as to obstruct chelation and forms no cupric complex (XIII).

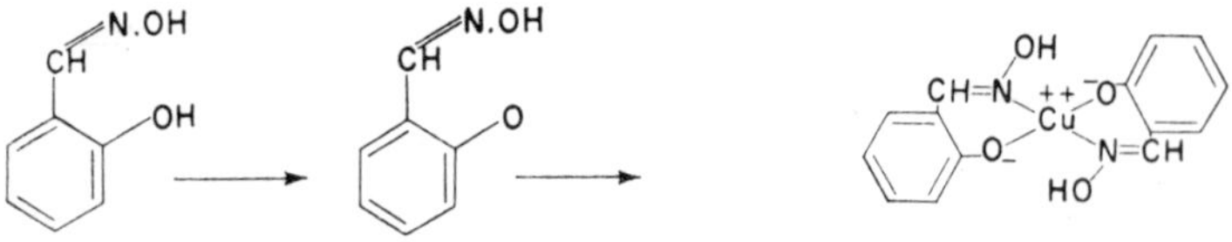

X

XI

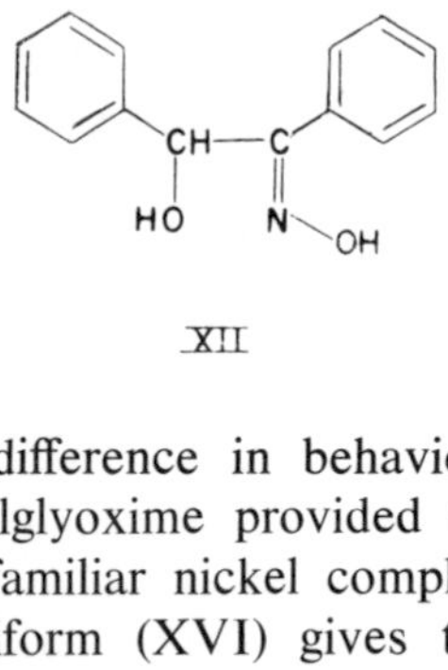

XII

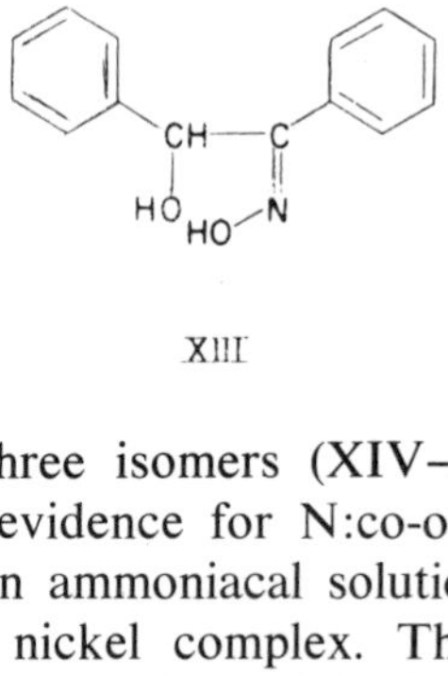

XIII

The difference in behaviour of the three isomers (XIV–XVI) of dimethylglyoxime provided the earliest evidence for N:co-ordination in the familiar nickel complex, formed in ammoniacal solution. Only the antiform (XVI) gives the pink-red nickel complex. The N:co-ordination has been confirmed by X-ray analysis, which also reveals

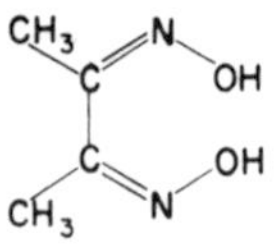

XIV

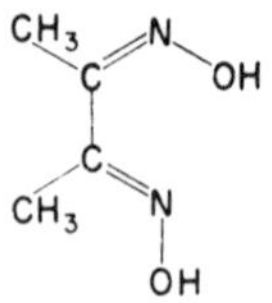

XV

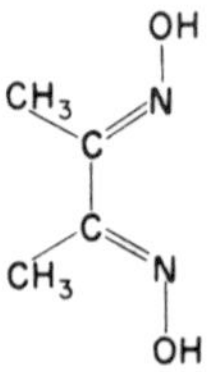

XVI

some peculiarities of this compound, resulting in its specificity for nickel under controlled conditions: one of the hydroxyl groups in each dimethylglyoxime molecule becomes ionized and hydrogen bond formation results in reinforcement of the chelation and planarity (XVII). In addition to this the molecules are so packed in the crystal that successive molecules lie above one another and the Ni—Ni distances are short enough to allow some orbital interaction in the long chain of nickel atoms so formed; it is this system, resulting from the d^8-structure of the Ni^{2+} ion, which is responsible for the unusual colour of the complex.

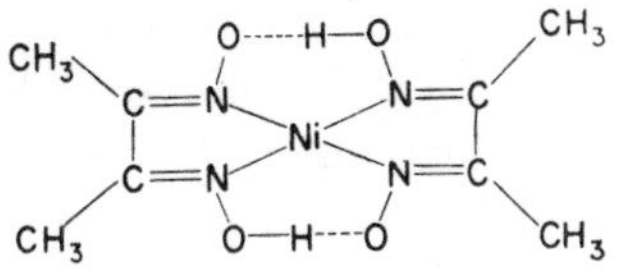

XVII

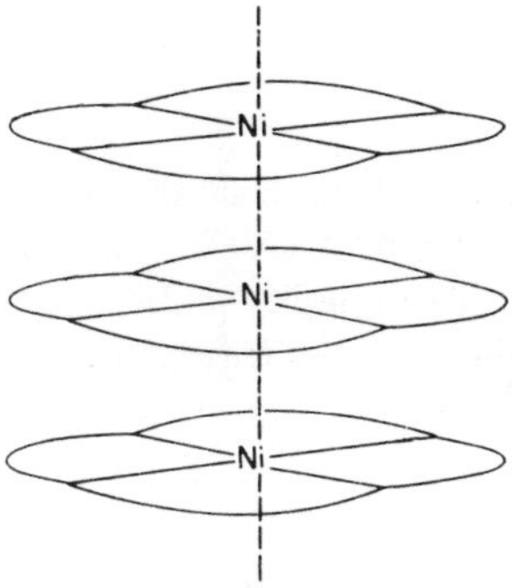

XVIII

In the reagent "cupferron" nitrosyl and hydroxyl groups are attached to the same aromatic amino nitrogen atom (XIX) and co-ordination occurs through the oxygen atoms (XX). First developed as a reagent for copper, this reagent is particularly valuable as a precipitant for iron, titanium or zirconium from strongly acid solutions, in which conditions aluminium, chromium, zinc, magnesium and most other metals do not react.

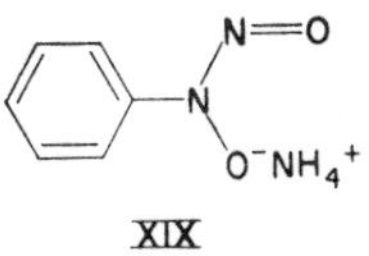

XIX

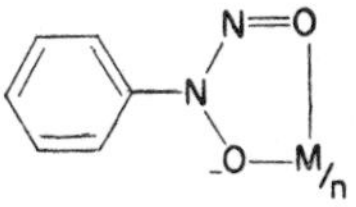

XX

The analogy often made between nitrosyl and carbonyl groups leads us to expect chelation by juxtaposed phenolic and ketonic groups. The most familiar examples are provided by the α-hydroxyanthraquinones which form "lakes" with many metal cations, particularly those forming amphoteric or very weakly basic hydroxides. Thus, in neutral or weakly alkaline solution, alizarin (XXI) gives blue- to red-coloured precipitates (lakes) with Al^{3+}, Sn^{4+}, Ti^{4+}, Be^{2+}, etc. As with the cobalt nitrosonaphthols, these coloured complexes can be solubilized by sulphonation and "alizarin red S" (XXII) is useful as a reagent, particularly for aluminium, zirconium and scandium, which give colours in neutral or slightly acid solutions. Decolorization of the zirconium lake by fluorides (which preferentially form the ZrF_6^{2-} complexion) may be used as a quantitative method for fluoride ions.

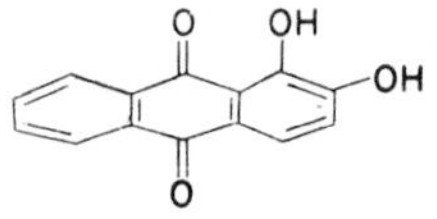

XXI 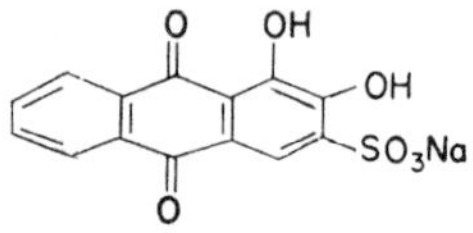 XXII

Carbonyl and acidic hydroxyl groups are also juxtaposed in the enolate ions (XXIV) of β-diketones, such as acetyl acetone (XXIII), which form highly stable inner complexes with many metals (XXV). The copper complex forms steely blue needles, soluble in organic solvents but not in water, and so resistant to thermal decomposition that it can be sublimed unchanged about 400°C. Many tetravalent ions exhibit their

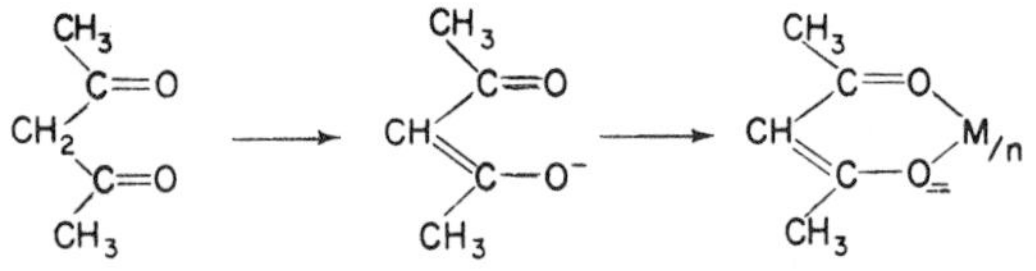

XXIII XXIV XXV

maximum covalency of eight in acetylacetonates such as $Zr(acac)_4$, $Ce(acac)_4$ and $Th(acac)_4$. The stabilities of these β-diketone complexes vary considerably with the nature of the ketones, benzoylacetone and dibenzoylmethane, for example, forming more stable complexes than acetylacetone, while those formed by trifluoracetylacetone and ethyl acetoacetate are of lower stability.

SOLVENT EXTRACTION

The electrical neutrality of inner complexes, which is responsible for their low solubility in water, frequently leads to an appreciable solubility in organic media; consequently, in the presence of ligands which can form inner complexes, many metals can be extracted into a water-immiscible organic phase, a process of value in both analytical and industrial separations.

The β-diketones, for example, have been applied to numerous separations. The best results have been obtained using the more acidic compounds such as trifluoracetylacetone (XXVI) or a α-thenoyltrifluoracetone (TTA, XXVII), by means of which a reasonably effective separation of zirconium and hafnium has been achieved, a process of great importance in removing hafnium (which has a high neutron capture cross-section) from zirconium for use in atomic reactors. Beryllium and scandium, also valuable nuclear engineering metals, have also been refined by solvent extraction in the presence of TTA.

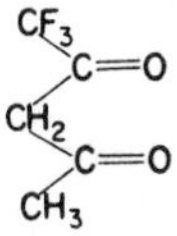

CF_3—C=O, CH_2, C=O, CH_3

XXVI

CF_3—C=O, CH_2, C=O, thienyl (S)

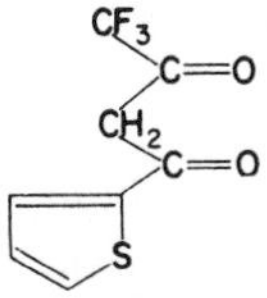

XXVII

Fundamentally, solvent extraction from aqueous solutions depends upon the competition of hydrogen ions and metal cations for the ligand anion (A^-):

$$OH_2 + HA \rightleftharpoons OH_3^+ + A^-$$
$$M^{n+} + nA^- \rightleftharpoons MA_n$$

The distribution of the metal between the phases thus depends on the acidity constant of the ligand acid and the stability constant of the inner complex and is sensitive to changes in pH. It is for this reason that the most satisfactory results are obtained with the more acidic ligands. It must be realized, however, that few extraction equilibria conform at all exactly to the simple distribution pattern derived from the above equations as complicating factors are nearly always present, such as solvation and polymerization effects, and even in some instances the slowness with which equilibrium is reached.

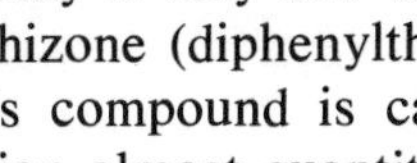

S=C(—NH—NH—C_6H_5)(—N=N—C_6H_5)

XXVIII

Many organic inner-complex forming ligands have been used in solvent extraction processes, but only a very few have proved of outstanding value. One of these is dithizone (diphenylthiocarbazone, XXVIII). A chloroform solution of this compound is capable of extracting many metals from aqueous solution almost quantitatively, and in some cases gives solutions of characteristic colour. It is particularly useful for the detection and estimation of lead, which gives a red chloroform solution, suitable for colorimetry. Zinc, which is simultaneously extracted into the chloroform layer, can be effectively separated by back-extraction with aqueous potassium thiocyanate. Iron, when present in large quantities, is usually removed by formation of the complex with cupferron (XX), which can be extracted with ether. Cupferron has also been used in the refinement of a number of metals by the solvent extraction method, including protoactinium, and oxine (III) has been made the basis of a number of separation processes, particularly of the metals of group IIIB.

These metals, however, are particularly well separated by ether extraction of solutions of their chlorides in strong hydrochloric acid: gallium is almost quantitatively extracted into the ether layer as $HGaCl_4$, while indium and aluminium remain in the aqueous layer, indium probably because of the lower stability of the $InCl_4^-$ complex ion and aluminium because the acid $HAlCl_4$ is too highly ionized; trivalent thallium accompanies gallium into the ether phase but is, of course, readily removed by reduction to the univalent state.

In the six-valent state molybdenum, likewise, is almost quantitatively extracted by ether from 6 N hydrochloric acid, leaving chromium and tungsten behind, but here more convenient methods of separation are available. Ether extraction from strong hydrochloric acid solution does, however, provide a convenient means of separating gold from all its neighbours, the gold passing into the organic phase as $HAuCl_4$; the extraction of gold is even more effective from hydrobromic acid solution.

Gold can also be extracted almost quantitatively by ether from 8 N nitric acid, dissolving in the organic phase presumably as the complex acid $HAu(NO_3)_4$, salts of which are known. So few metals form stable nitrate complexes that extraction from strong nitric acid solutions by organic oxygenated solvents such as ether, ketones or phosphates provides nearly specific methods for the refinement of these metals. Only tetravalent cerium, which forms stable 6:co-ordinated complex nitrates, is extracted as effectively as gold, presumably as $H_2Ce(NO_3)_6$; some 35% of thorium is extracted under the same conditions and about 65% of six-valent uranium (as uranyl nitrate) and this method has been used for the refinement of uranium for atomic energy purposes. Extraction of these metals occurs only from very strong nitric acid solutions, possibly because of the suppression of ionization of the complex-nitrate acids; it is not affected by highly ionized nitrates, such as KNO_3 or $Ba(NO_3)_2$, but is facilitated by the presence of some other nitrates, notably those of ferric iron, zinc and lithium, suggesting that non-ionized or slightly ionized double nitrates may be formed, such as $Li_2Ce(NO_3)_6$, but our knowledge of the detailed physical chemistry of these systems is still slight.

SEQUESTRATION

Considerable use has been made of the ability of co-ordinating groups to suppress the normal reactions of metal cations. In the presence of complex-forming ligands, an equilibrium:

$$M^{n+} + xL \rightleftharpoons ML_x^{n+}$$

is set up and reduces the concentration of M^{n+} ions in solution, thus preventing reactions, such as precipitation processes, which depend on the concentration of free cations. The extent to which reactions are inhibited depends on the stability constants of the complexes formed and the solubility product of the precipitate.

Familiar examples of this "sequestering" power from routine analytical procedures include the precipitation of bismuth as the hydroxide, $Bi(OH)_3$, by ammonia in the presence of copper and cadmium, which are held in solution as the ammines $[Cu(NH_3)_4]^{2+}$ and $[Cd(NH_3)_4]^{2+}$, and the separation of copper from cadmium by the action of hydrogen sulphide on solutions of the complex cyanides, $[Cu(CN)_4]^{3-}$ and $[Cd(CN)_4]^{2-}$, only the cadmium complex giving the insoluble sulphide under these conditions. The interference of organic acids in qualitative analysis is also due to the comparatively high stabilities of the complexes which are formed with ions such as Al^{3+} and Fe^{3+}, and advantage is taken of the complexing power of tartaric acid in several analytical procedures: in mineral analysis, for example, iron may be separated from aluminium, titanium and zirconium by precipitation with hydrogen sulphide from ammoniacal tartrate solution, when the iron is reduced to the divalent state and precipitates as ferrous sulphide, while the presence of the tartrate prevents the precipitation of the other metals as hydroxides. Yet another example of the application of organic acids is the separation of calcium and magnesium in the presence of an excess of oxalate, calcium oxalate remaining undissolved, whilst the magnesium goes into solution as the oxalato-complex $[Mg(C_2O_4)_2]^{2-}$.

The term "sequestration", however, is usually used to refer to the suppression of those precipitation reactions of calcium and magnesium which are responsible for the "hardening" of water. The precipitation of soaps as their calcium or magnesium salts by hard water can be prevented by the complexing of the metal cations; the formation of scale, consequent on the boiling of temporarily hard water, and dependent on the reactions:

$$2HCO_3^- = H_2O + CO_2 + CO_3^{2-}$$
$$M^{2+} + CO_3^{2-} = MCO_3$$

can be similarly prevented, but, of course, the accumulation of solids in boilers, due to the evaporation of water, cannot be controlled in this way.

In practice, two main types of complexing agent have been used for the sequestration of calcium and magnesium ions in water: phosphates and polydentate aminoacids.

The addition of certain phosphates to hard water produces precipitates of calcium and magnesium salts which redissolve on addition of excess of the phosphate solution, probably due to complex formation; in the presence of the excess of phosphate soaps give no precipitate, so that the water has been effectively softened. The effectiveness of the phosphates as sequestering agents depends upon the nature of the phosphate anion: orthophosphates have very little effect and indeed, sodium orthophosphate will not redissolve the precipitate of calcium orthophosphate produced. The sequestering power of the polyphosphates is much greater, the most satisfactory results being obtained with the polyphosphate glasses in the composition range $Na_2O:P_2O_5 = 1:1{\cdot}1\text{–}1{\cdot}3$, where the molecular weight of the anion corresponds to a chain length of from four to eight units, sometimes referred to as "hexametaphosphate". The precise nature of the phosphate complexes formed is not known.

Polydentate amino acids, such as nitrilotriacetic acid and ethylene-diamine-tetra-acetic acid (EDTA) also form highly stable complexes with Mg^{2+} and Ca^{2+} ions and are widely used in water softening, the latter being known commercially as "sequestrene" or "complexone". The extraordinary stability of the EDTA complexes arises from the possibility of forming from the same ligand up to five five-membered chelate ring systems (XXIX) and is high enough to prevent the precipitation of calcium or magnesium by all ordinary reagents and even of barium by sulphate.

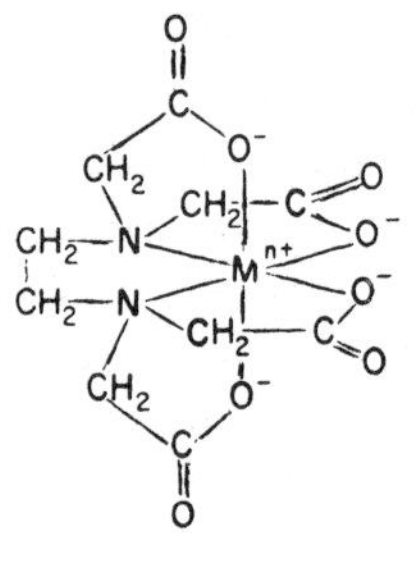

XXIX

EDTA is also used as a titrant for the volumetric estimation of calcium, magnesium and other metals, indicators being based on the principle of competitive complex formation by complex-forming dyes. The indicator solochrome black (XXX), for instance, gives a blue solution in water at pH 6·3–11·5 but forms a wine-red complex with calcium or magnesium ions. On addition of EDTA to the wine-red solution, the metal ions are removed by preferential complex formation and when the last trace of metal ion has been removed the blue colour of the indicator reappears. With murexide (XXXI) as indicator, magnesium forms no coloured complex but calcium forms a pink complex, the colour of which gives way to the blue colour of the indicator anion when the calcium is preferentially complexed on addition of EDTA. Other metals can be titrated by adding more than enough EDTA to complex them and back titrating the excess with magnesium or calcium, as in the titrimetric finish to the estimation of lead or barium as sulphate.

Closely related to the sequestration processes are those which involve adsorption or desorption of ions on zeolites or ion-exchange resins. Such processes have long been in use for the removal of calcium and magnesium from hard water, the zeolite or resin acting as an anchored complexing framework, which co-ordinates the more highly-charged Ca^{2+} and Mg^{2+} ions in preference to sodium ions. The most spectacular results have been achieved, however, in the separation of the lanthanide elements.

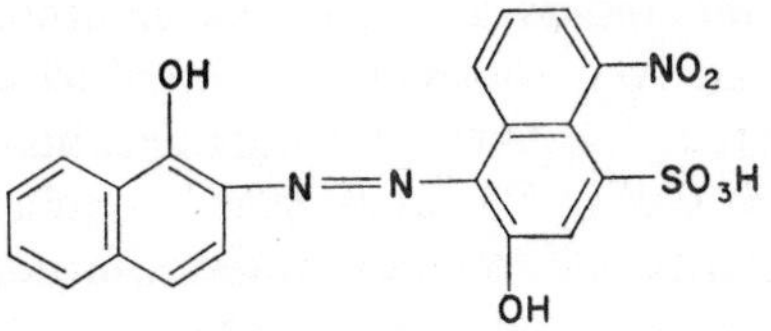

XXX

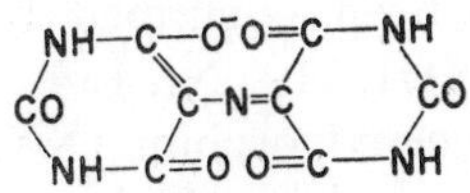

XXXI

We should expect that those lanthanide ions which are of smaller radius would be more effectively adsorbed on ion-exchange resins, but in practice it is not possible to obtain a satisfactory separation by the simple process of adsorption followed by elution with water or dilute acid. Very effective separation has been obtained, however, by the competitive method: the metals are first adsorbed on the resin and eluted with a solution of a complexing anion, the order of appearance in the eluent depending on the stabilities of the complexes formed. In the earliest experiments of this type citrate was used as eluent, but even better results have been obtained using nitrilotriacetate, EDTA or other amino acid or hydroxyamino acid complexing agents.

PORPHYRINS AND RELATED COMPOUNDS

A variety of co-ordination compounds has been found to have importance biologically. The best known of these is the group of metal derivatives of the pyrrole pigments known as porphyrins. These include the iron complexes occurring in the red colouring matter of blood, the magnesium complexes in chlorophyll and the cobalt complex in vitamin B12. Manganese, vanadium and copper porphyrins have also been found in nature.

The metal porphyrins are derived from porphin (XXXII) by substitution of a metal atom for the two central hydrogen atoms (XXXIII) and differ from one another in the substituents in the porphin ring.

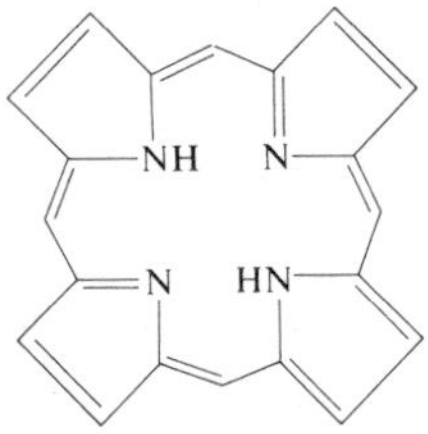

XXXII 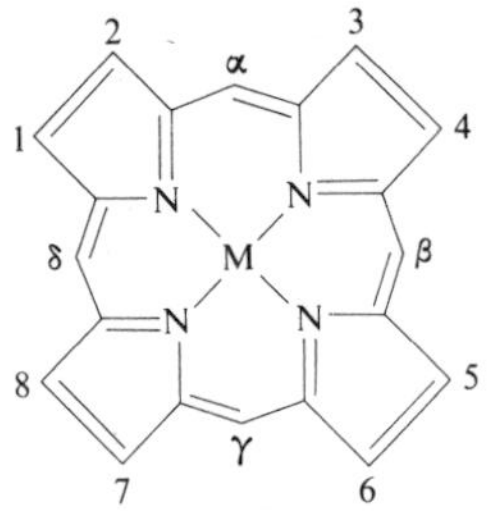 XXXIII

The central position of the metal atom and its square-planar environment have been confirmed by X-ray analysis of nickel etioporphyrin(II) (XXXIII, M = Ni; 1, 4, 5, 8 methyl; 2, 3, 6, 7 ethyl) and copper and zinc tetraphenylporphins (XXXIII, M = Cu or Zn, α, β, γ, δ phenyl); zinc tetraphenylporphin has an additional two water molecules co-ordinated to the zinc atom, above and below the porphin plane, though the rather long Zn—O distance of 2·45 Å suggests that these water molecules are not very firmly attached.

Very similar in structure to the porphyrins are the phthalocyanin pigments. These were discovered accidentally when it was found that some samples of phthalimide made in an iron vessel were contaminated with a blue iron-containing pigment. Copper phthalocyanine (XXXIV) can be readily obtained by heating powdered copper metal with phthalonitrile at 190°C.

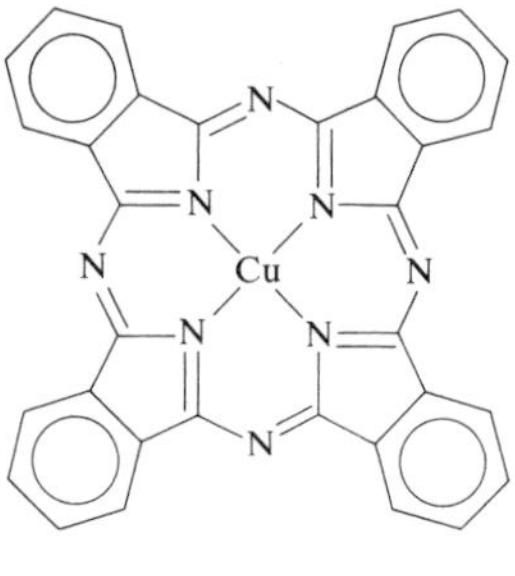

XXXIV 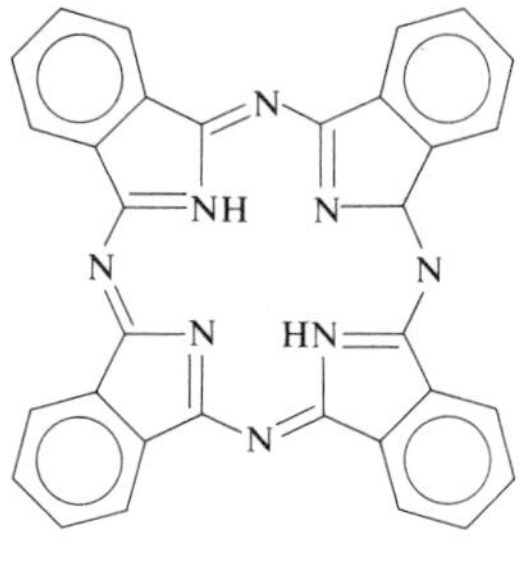 XXXV

Metal-free phthalocyanine (XXXV) can be obtained from the magnesium or lead compounds by the action of acid. This and the nickel and platinum complexes have been shown to be planar structures by X-ray analysis.

The metal–porphyrin and phthalocyanine pigments thus form a group of complex compounds in which square-planar stereochemistry is forced on the metal atom by the geometry of the ligand. When the metal atom has a preference for higher co-ordination numbers, additional ligands become co-ordinated above or below the molecular plane. Both 5:- and 6:co-ordinate compounds of this type are known. Naturally occurring porphyrins, such as haemin, are combined with protein material by co-ordination of a protein nitrogen atom in one of these sites. In haemoglobin, the sixth site on the iron atom can be occupied by small donor molecules such as water, oxygen or carbon monoxide. The affinity of metallo-porphyrins for additional ligands depends on the metal atom; thus iron(II) porphyrins take on additional ligands much more strongly than iron(III) porphyrins and the oxygen-carrying ability of haemoglobin appears to depend on absorption of oxygen molecules by the iron(II) complex and their loss after oxidation of the iron(II) to iron(III). The process is, however, more complicated than this as aquo-iron(II) haemoglobin has the high-spin configuration ($\mu = 4{\cdot}47\beta$) but the oxygen, carbon monoxide and cyanide complexes have low-spin configurations ($\mu = 0\beta$).

The ability to act as oxygen carriers has also been observed in some related compounds. Thus manganese(II) phthalocyanine in pyridine solution absorbs oxygen reversibly and from the oxygenated solution a compound can be isolated which may be represented as oxo-pyridine-manganese(IV) phthalocyanine. The cobalt(II) complex of the Schiff's base ethylenediamine-bis-salicylaldehyde also acts as an oxygen carrier and in this compound the cobalt atom is also at the centre of a ligand

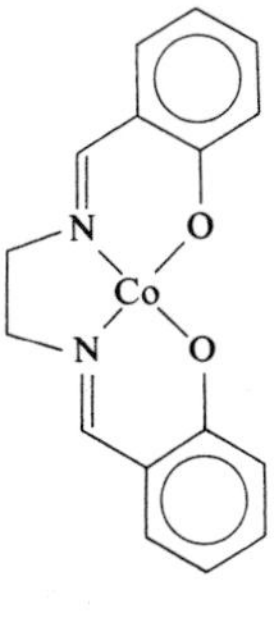

XXXVI

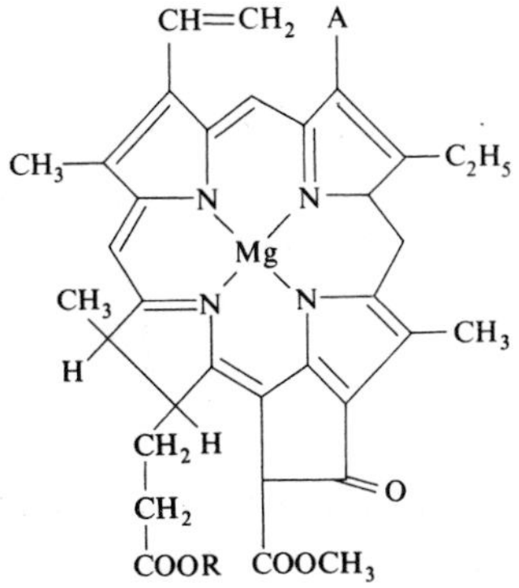

XXXVII

which will tend to impose square planar stereochemistry with the possibility of adding extra ligands above and below the molecular plane (XXVI). Crystal structures of some related compounds have been determined and are discussed in Chapter III.

Reduction potentials have been determined for a number of metal–porphyrin systems. Complexing by porphyrins has been found invariably to stabilize the upper oxidation state, the extent of stabilization varying from about 0·6 V for iron protoporphyrin (1:3:5:8-tetramethyl 2:4-vinyl-6:7-carboxyethyl) to more than 2·0 V for some cobalt complexes. The reduction potential is also sensitive to changes of the ligands in the fifth and sixth positions and, in most cases, to variations in pH.

In haem-type porphyrins the $\alpha, \beta, \gamma, \delta$ carbon atoms are unsubstituted, but some other naturally occurring complexes involve substitution in these sites. In the chlorophylls, one of these positions is linked to a neighbouring carbon atom to form an additional five-membered ring, and one of the pyrrole rings is saturated at the peripheral carbon atoms (XXXVII, R = phytyl, A = CH_3 in chlorophyll *a*, CHO in chlorophyll *b*). It has been shown that the magnesium atom is capable of further co-ordination with bases such as water, alcohols or amines, but it is apparently not known whether such further co-ordination occurs in nature or is involved in the sugar-synthesizing reactions for which chlorophyll is necessary.

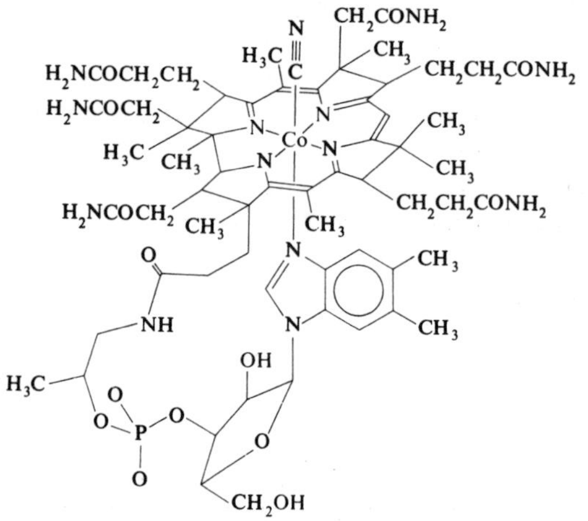

XXXVIII

Vitamin B12, the complete structure of which has been determined by X-ray analysis, provides a further variation in structure of the porphyrin ring. In addition to extensive saturation, one of the bridges has been replaced by a direct link, and two of the other bridges are substituted

(XXXVIII). The cobalt atom has an octahedral environment completed by co-ordination of a benzimidazole nitrogen and a cyanide group. In the closely related cobamide coenzymes the cyanide group is replaced by adenosine, and other derivatives are known in which either the cyanide or benzimidazole groups, or both, are replaced by various other groups.

The role of the metal atom in these and other enzymes is not known with any certainty, but metal atoms are commonly an essential part of enzymes, and this seems likely to be the reason for the importance of trace quantities of metals in the food of animals and plants. A variety of modes of action have been suggested. In the simplest case the metal may be associated with the enzyme only loosely, perhaps attaching it to the substrate during the process of catalysis; this apparently occurs in the association of magnesium with phosphatase and zinc with enolase. A number of enzymes, however, contain metal atoms when isolated, and these metal atoms may be more or less easily removed. Thus molybdenum, which is present in nitrate reductase, dissociates readily but zinc, present in alcohol dehydrogenase, does not readily dissociate, though the activity of the enzyme is inhibited by chelating agents such as 1:10-phenanthroline; succinic acid dehydrogenase, which contains iron, provides a more extreme example since its action is not affected by such chelating agents.

The most likely function of the metal atom in these systems is to act as a link between the enzyme and the substrate by either increasing the co-ordination number of the metal atom by co-ordination of an atom in the substrate, or by replacement of a loosely co-ordinated group such as a water molecule by a substrate atom. Examples of both types of behaviour are provided by the porphyrin complexes. When an enzyme is involved in an oxidation or reduction process, there is the further possibility that the metal atom may be involved in electron-transfer reactions, for example, by providing a pathway for one-electron transfer. There is some evidence for change of oxidation state of copper and iron in systems of this type, but our knowledge of the functions of trace metals in biological systems is still rudimentary.

FURTHER READING

FALK, J. E., *Porphyrins and Metalloporphyrins*, Elsevier, Amsterdam (1964).
KITCHENER, J. A., *Ion-exchange Resins*, Methuen, London (1957).
PERRIN, D. D., *Organic Complexing Reagents*, John Wiley, New York (1965).

BONNETT, R., The vitamin B12 group, *Chem. Rev.* **63**, 573 (1963).
BRAY, R. C. and HARRAP, K. R. Metals and enzymes, *Chem. Soc. Ann. Rep.* 343 (1962).
CALVIN, M., Coordination chemistry of manganese and porphyrins, *Rev. Pure Appl. Chem.* **15**, 1 (1965).
DWYER, F. P., Enzyme-metal ion activation and catalytic phenomena with metal complexes, *Chelating Agents and Metal Chelates*, Eds. MELLOR, D. P. and DWYER, F. P., Academic Press, New York (1964).

DWYER, F. P. and SHULMAN, A., Metal chelates in biological systems, *ibid.*

IRVING, H. M., The application of solvent extraction to inorganic analysis, *Quart. Rev.* **5**, 200 (1951).

MARTIN, F. S. and HOLT, R. J. W., Liquid–liquid extraction in inorganic chemistry, *Quart. Rev.* **13**, 327 (1959).

PERUTZ, M. F., The anatomy of haemoglobin, *Chem. Brit.* 9 (1965).

VAN WAZER, J. R. and CALLIS, C. F., Metal complexing by phosphates, *Chem. Rev.* **58**, 1011 (1958).

WHITE, A. M., Vitamin B12, *Chem. Soc. Ann. Rep.* 400 (1962).

AUTHOR INDEX

SUBJECT INDEX